Home or Nursing Home

Making the Right Choices

Second Edition

Michael J. Salamon, PhD, a Fellow of the American Psychological Association and the Gerontological Society of America, has been involved in the field of adult development for over 25 years. Dr. Salamon has worked in both community and institutional settings as an administrator, clinician, researcher, and educator. He has published extensively and is the author of the text, *A Basic Guide to Working with Elders,* and is the senior author of the *Salamon–Conte Life Satisfaction in the Elderly Scale.* Dr. Salamon serves as the executive director of the Adult Developmental Center of Hewlett, New York, a private organization that he helped establish. Through his work with the Adult Developmental Center, Dr. Salamon has been a consultant to a variety of professional groups in the United States and abroad. He has served as professional advisor to a number of radio and television shows. He has also served on the executive board of Psychologists in Long-Term Care, and is on the editorial board of *Clinical Gerontologist.*

Gloria Rosenthal, author of four nonfiction books, contributes regularly to *Lupus Chronicle* online, and writes extensively for a variety of national publications, including medical, women's, and general-interest magazines, in which she covers such diverse topics as health, disabilities, child care, and theater. She has made numerous television appearances in connection with her books and articles, and she presents seminars on language and written communication through her company, World of Words.

Home or Nursing Home

Making the Right Choices

Second Edition

Michael J. Salamon, PhD

Gloria Rosenthal

 Springer Publishing Company

Springer Publishing Company, Inc.
536 Broadway
New York, NY 10012-3955

Acquisitions Editor: Shoshana Bauminger
Production Editor: Betsy Day
Cover design by Joanne Honigman

04 05 06 07 08 / 5 4 3 2 1

Library of Congress Cataloging-in-Publication Data

Salamon, Michael J.
    Home or nursing home : making the right choices / Michael J. Salamon, Gloria Rosenthal. — 2nd ed.
      p. cm.
    Includes bibliographical references and index.
    ISBN 0-8261-6681-4
    1. Home care services. 2. Nursing homes. 3. Aged—Medical care.
I. Rosenthal, Gloria. II. Title.

RA645.3.S25 2004
362.16—dc22
                                              2003057105

Printed in the United States of America by Integrated Books.

For my grandmother, Golda Kessler, who was well cared for during her final days in a nursing home. By coincidence, my first clinical position was in that same nursing home.
—Michael J. Salamon

For my mother, Lillian K. Weiss, who lived her last years in a nursing home in good cheer and healthy spirit.
—Gloria Rosenthal

Contents

Acknowledgments

The research that went into making this second edition of *Home or Nursing Home* a reality was 20 years in the making. Without the assistance of the many physicians, nurses, therapists, administrators, patients, residents and family members who took part in the several studies cited, this work could not have been completed. Not only did the patients agree to participate but they also encouraged me to continue my work; I am most grateful to them. There is a great divide, however, between gathering and reporting data and presenting it in a context that is useful to both clinicians and the public. I was able to accomplish that only because of the efforts of several key individuals. Our secretaries, Mary Famulare and Ellen Moore, finished their work in record time. Indra Sinanan, my right hand, typed, did research, proofed and did all that was necessary to get the job done. The people at Springer Publishing, in particular Dr. Ursula Springer, Shoshana Bauminger, and Betsy Day, who encouraged a second edition and helped bring it to fruition, are owed a debt of gratitude. Most of all, I would like to thank my own director of quality management, Naomi M. Salamon, RN. In addition to being a long-term care specialist with a warm heart, she is my long-term best friend, cheerleader, and motivator.

MICHAEL J. SALAMON, PhD

Introduction

When *Home or Nursing Home* first came out, both positive and negative reactions were many. Few faulted the research, but most were critical of the idea that nursing homes could be viewed positively. Since then, ongoing research seems to support the *Life Satisfaction in the Elderly Scale* (revised to *Life Satisfaction Scale*). Nursing homes may not be an appropriate choice in many situations. There are options, but, when there are none, a nursing home may be the best intervention.

One of the most prevalent beliefs regarding long-term care is that frail elderly individuals can never be as happy or as well cared for as they can be at home. Nursing homes are often seen as a last resort. These perceptions, as we see in this text, are not necessarily accurate. In fact, several studies strongly suggest that, in many cases, the nursing home option is the better choice for care of a frail elderly loved one. Many ideas regarding illness and caring for ailing elders are incorrect and based on misinformation, fear of the unknown, and preconceived notions from the past—notions not necessarily true in the present. Some of the more popular misconceptions follow.

More people die in nursing homes than anywhere else. This statement is true, but it is misleading. More people may die in nursing home than at home, but that is because the people who live there tend to be sicker than those in the general population. Recent research suggests that, on average, these very ill individuals residing in nursing homes may in fact live longer in that environment than they would have at home. Also, the nursing home often becomes a permanent residence, and it is to be anticipated that more people will live out their years in this setting. People who live at home are often transferred to hospitals, where they die, thereby spuriously reducing the rates of expiration at home.

When you take a relative to a nursing home, you are dumping him or her! There are, of course, instances in which older people are dumped into the care of a nursing home. This may occur when there are no relatives or the relationship between relatives is strained. In most cases, however, the reason for seeking care in a nursing home setting is a desire to seek the best possible care for someone who has a chronic illness that requires ongoing medical supervision and constant nursing care, which cannot be provided elsewhere. In some instances, home care may be the best option. In other cases, however, nursing home care may be preferable, and choosing this option is not analogous to dumping an unwanted relative.

Nursing homes are hellholes, "snake pits," and so forth. Well over two decades ago, there were scandalous incidents of fraud, improper care, and patient abuse, but these cases now tend to be less likely. Government intervention, in the form of constant and regular supervision, has significantly reduced such horror stories.

When investigative reports suggest that nursing homes are not providing proper care, they are usually referring to a small proportion of all nursing homes. Approximately one in four nursing homes is cited each year for causing injury, but it is hoped that, in the future, even this percentage will be completely eliminated. Furthermore, when a nursing home is the best choice for a loved one, knowing what to look for, as detailed in this book, will make it easier to select a facility dedicated to the care of its residents.

Patients in nursing homes sit and stare vacantly, with nothing to occupy their time and minds. Although many patients cannot interact because of physical or emotional conditions, all tend to benefit from the social environment, which provides, at the very least, constant stimulation by a variety of care providers. Indeed, most states have laws governing how much time nursing home patients can remain in bed or in their rooms and at what time they should be dressed in the morning. In addition, those who are able may take advantage of recreational activities, also mandated by law. Every nursing home must have an activity director and a recreation program. The schedule of activities must be posted on all floors for the patients to see. The staff hired for the sole purpose of providing these activities will encourage patients to learn new hobbies, practice old ones, and become involved in musical activities and discussion groups.

Several studies have found that individuals who reside in nursing homes are more satisfied with social contacts and their lives in general than individuals receiving health care elsewhere.

Nursing homes do not provide the personal care patients need. In many cases, nursing homes provide superior care, catering to the specific needs of each patient: 24-hour nursing care and a range of therapeutic programs, such as physical therapy, occupational therapy, speech therapy and audiology, and social services. Nursing homes also have dietary departments that must daily serve nutritious meals. The facility must also provide clean beds and a protected environment. Home care, even with the most devoted attention and visiting health services, often cannot compete with the supervision and sophisticated equipment that nursing homes, by law, must furnish.

The unlicensed "snake pit" of the past is almost extinct, and today it is easy to use definite guidelines to select a fine, reputable, safe nursing home.

You may be surprised to learn that recent studies indicate that patients in nursing homes recognize their own limitations and, despite these limitations, are often satisfied, content, even happy, with their lives. In the aged, happiness can be objectively measured by the use of tools such as the Life Satisfaction in the Elderly Scale (LSES)—now called Life Satisfaction Scale (LSS), because the norms were expanded. Results of recent research indicate that patients in nursing homes generally attain greater satisfaction with their lives than equivalent patients receiving care at home.

Certainly there are many cases in which home care is more than adequate, even preferable, but, when patients require constant skilled–nursing care, there is often no substitute for the nursing home setting, especially the right type of nursing home. In the following chapters, we explore many aspects of health care for the elderly. We discuss the ever increasing aging population and provide answers to many important questions that client families often ask—the primary one being, *What do we do about Mama?*

We define and describe all the options, from private physicians to outpatient clinics to skilled–nursing facilities (SNF), and everything in between. We also analyze many of the reasons—sometimes valid, sometimes not—for health care choices. Findings from the previously mentioned studies of life satisfaction will furnish some important and revealing information about how the elderly view themselves in relation to their health care environments. Conclusions drawn from the studies will help those who must make decisions about health care in a time of crisis. In clear, nontechnical terms, we present advice, along with case histories of typical situations. For those who are still having trouble making the decision, **Chapter 7** contains a quiz designed to point out the advantages and disadvantages of home care and the pluses and minuses of nursing home care.

This text was originally written for health care professionals—the doctors, nurses, counselors, and social workers who must help their clients make some very difficult decisions. Over the years, the text has developed a following among a general audience, and is listed as recommended reading by many long-term care advocacy programs. We trust that the information provided will be enlightening and helpful at a time when crucial decisions must be made.

MICHAEL J. SALAMON
GLORIA ROSENTHAL

Chapter 1

Health Care Needs of the Elderly

AN EXAMPLE

Bertha R. was 78 years old when her husband died in his sleep. The death certificate listed the cause as a heart attack. Bertha and Jack had been married 58 years; they had two sons, two daughters, and nine grandchildren. Never wealthy, they had lived a decent life in the same neighborhood for almost 40 years. For the past 10 years or so, they had been involved in social activities with longtime friends and neighbors. They went to the senior center every other day, attended adult education lectures at the high school twice a week, and often visited with their children, who always welcomed them. In short, they had a good life, a pleasant life, and an active life.

A few weeks after Jack's funeral, when friends stopped visiting or extending their condolences, Bertha began to feel very much alone and lonely. She decided to spend a few weeks with one of her sons, and before anyone realized it, she had stayed several months. She enjoyed the family, and they enjoyed having her. Besides, she was a wonderful babysitter. Her visit was cut short abruptly one morning when she did not see a roller skate on her way to the bathroom: Bertha fell and broke her hip.

She was in the hospital for several weeks and progressed well. Her hip healed nicely, but the doctors told her that because of the type of break she had suffered and the condition of her bones, she would need intensive physical therapy. Furthermore, she would have to restrict some activities and should avoid stairs as much as possible for a while. Her children decided that she would move in with Marilyn, the youngest daughter. Marilyn's house was the largest and had the fewest number of stairs. Because her mother was not seriously ill, Marilyn did not give up her job, and her teenage children did not turn down their stereos or reduce their comings and goings. Their friends continued to drop in often, as they always did.

Bertha was walking much better after just a few months, but her overall condition had begun to deteriorate. She always seemed tired and became just a little angry—something that was very uncharacteristic of her. Her children tried to get her involved in activities, but she showed little interest in anything. She spoke of wanting to go home, but her children reminded her many times that, while she was in the hospital, they had decided—and she had agreed—to let her apartment go. Soon, Bertha suffered an intestinal obstruction and needed surgery. This time she was in the hospital much longer, and when she came out, she had a temporary colostomy bag. She was bewildered and confused.

Now always angry, Bertha snapped and yelled at her children, grandchildren, and the aides hired to care for her.

One night, while everyone slept, Bertha dressed herself quickly and sloppily, placing a sweater over her nightgown; tying a belt around her waist, she went for a walk. The police found her two days later. She was disheveled and disoriented; she did not know where she had been and was no longer sure of her children's names. Bertha was hospitalized again for evaluation, and, within a few days, despite medication changes, the doctors told the children that their mother was not likely to show much improvement. Her worn-out, frustrated children knew the time had come to consider placement of some sort. They were told that, because of Mom's condition and her ongoing need for rehabilitation, they should consider a nursing home. It was a long, slow process, but they finally found a place that was nearby, clean, and of good reputation.

The first few weeks in the nursing home, Bertha protested and complained, but she slowly began to show an interest in the activities offered. She seemed happier; her anger began to dissipate, and a good deal of her old sparkle returned. On one of her visits, Marilyn saw her mother watching a television sitcom with her peers and heard her mother laugh. "I would never have believed it," Marilyn said. "It's been months since she's even smiled."

DEMOGRAPHICS OF AN AGING POPULATION

Bertha's story is not an isolated one. Nor is it a story that people in the early 1900s would have heard. In those days, the average person lived about 45 to 50 years. Only about 4% of the population reached age 65 (U.S. Census, 1982). There were so few Berthas around that caring for the elderly was not a prime concern of families. At the turn of the century, children expected that, by the time they grew up and had families of their own, their parents would be gone. It was an accepted fact of life and death. At that time, health care consisted almost entirely of family doctors. Those doctors made house calls, their little black leather bags holding the most modern technology of the times. Hospitals were not the sterile environments they are today, and patients were sent to them with little expectation for survival. Nursing homes as we know them were unheard-of, because there was nobody to inhabit them, and, although poorhouses existed, they were not so much for the elderly and feeble as the socially and economically destitute.

Today, people live well beyond 45 or 50 years, and they live well. It is not unusual to hear of someone embarking on a second career or a second marriage at an age when his grandparents had already died. At the age of 45 or 50, people now enter the stage of midlife crisis. The term *midlife* suggests many more years of productive living, and, as Gail Sheehy noted several years ago, "The new middle-aged no longer think sick" (Sheehy, 1986, p. 345). In fact, definitions of the age of onset of midlife are changing from approximately 40 to approximately 50 and the shift from being middle-aged to old is now more a function of health than chronology (Lachman & James, 1997; Willis & Reid, 1999).

Currently, life expectancy is in the late 70s, closing in on 80, and is still climbing steadily (Administration on Aging, 2001). Of course, many individuals exceed these averages, and, once a person has passed age 65, the chance of outliving the statistics is greatly increased. Years ago, the death of a 70-year-old evoked comments such as "He lived a long life," "His time was up," and "He was lucky to have lived so long." Today, the words heard at the funeral of a person in his 70s are drastically changed: "He was too young," "He had years ahead of him," "He was still so vital," or "He didn't even get a chance to enjoy his retirement."

This extension of the life span, the result in no small measure of advances in sciences and medical know-how, has its obvious rewards. Older people are not only alive at the birth of their grandchildren, but they are also around to attend confirmations and bar/bat mitzvahs, to be present at high school or even college graduations, and to dance at their grandchildren's weddings—an occurrence unheard of in previous generations. Where our grandparents, if living, were too frail to attend our school plays, our children's grandparents go bicycle riding, play tennis, and work out at health spas. According to an Associated Press report in July 1986, Ginger Rogers, on her 75th birthday, was traveling from her

Palm Springs home to her Oregon ranch, a three-day auto trip. She played tennis and golf every day and was considering an offer to star on the London stage. Lucille Ball, 75, was starting a new television series, and Bob Hope, in his 80s, showed no signs of retiring. And who would be surprised to see George Burns starring in his own centennial celebration? Many celebrities today are proving that life can go on and that they can be productive well into their later years. Mike Wallace, at age 84, reported 20 stories from *60 Minutes* in the 2001 season and still makes public appearances: Julia Child appeared on *Larry King Live* on her 90th birthday in 2002. These are the celebrities we hear about, but there are just as many people who do not make the news: brokers, doctors, lawyers, and nonprofessionals in their 70s and 80s still maintaining active practices.

NORMAL BIOLOGICAL AND EMOTIONAL CHANGES

Along with the rewards of increasing longevity, however, come the problems. Young married couples rearing their own children are faced with the mounting demands of older parents who require unusual care and attention (Zarit, Reever, & Bache-Peterson, 1980; Zarit, 1996). An older person still vigorous despite advancing years, may have to cope with a frail spouse, and nieces and nephews may find themselves caring for an elderly childless aunt (Kaye, 1997; Morrow-Howell, Proctor, Dore, & Kaplan, 1998; Strawbridge & Wallhagen, 1992). Uncles seldom become caregivers because women usually outlive men, and the widowers who do survive into old age often remarry (Kosberg & Kaye, 1997).

Then there are the normal biological changes that come with increasing age: loss of bone strength; decreasing lung capacity; the general slowing-down of the cardiovascular system. These changes do not necessarily indicate illness, but many of these conditions require medical intervention and perhaps ongoing care. However, they are rarely life-threatening and, as we know, can be well compensated for (Blazer, 1990; Rowe & Kahn, 1998). The heart may pump harder to counteract the slowing of the cardiovascular system; the body tires more quickly, to prevent overexertion; and even the shrinking of the skeletal system, which in extreme cases is referred to as "dowager's hump," conceivably has a purpose: Like a tree that bends in the breeze, the body that shrinks ever so slightly is less subject to the stresses placed on it by the constant pull of gravity.

Modern health care and technological advances also help the body to compensate for the normal changes of aging. Vision problems caused by changes in the elasticity of the eyes are corrected with eyeglasses. Hearing aids, dentures, even total hip replacements, make up for nature's flaws, giving the body additional comfortable years. Take the case of Esther H., 72, whose hipbone joints had degenerated because of arthritis. Two months after a total hip replacement operation, Esther, a social worker, was back at work, walking without a limp and going to her dance class every Thursday evening.

Sometimes, biological changes are accompanied by emotional upset, even depression (Alexopoulos, 1996; Leibson et al., 1999). Individuals proud of their hearing acuity may feel a loss of self-esteem when they first learn of the need to wear a hearing aid. People who have suffered heart attacks may temporarily feel and act depressed, even after a rapid, successful rehabilitation (Bookwala & Schulz, 1996; Winokur, Black, & Nasrallah, 1988). For the most part, however, these negative emotions and reactive depressions can be replaced by positive feelings, when people realize they are no longer seriously threatened (Mosher-Ashley & Barrett, 1997). For example, as the physical condition of the 74-year-old man who underwent heart-bypass surgery improved, so that he was able to return to work and to his beloved golf, so too did his emotional condition.

If not properly prepared for, retirement itself may be responsible for many emotional changes (Palmore, 1984; Monk, 1997). Along with a loss of self-worth, there is an overpowering feeling of uselessness that comes from suddenly having nowhere to go in the morning. A person who has been admired, respected, and acknowledged on a daily basis, in a field or profession of importance to that person, is suddenly made to feel that he or she has nothing to offer. This can be a shattering blow to one's psyche. Here too, there are, fortunately, compensatory mechanisms. The 65-year-old no longer needs to retire completely; he or she can go into another field, do volunteer work, or find interesting hobbies. Several companies are experimenting with flextime and partial-retirement programs, allowing older workers to set flexible work schedules, providing them with time for relaxation, as well as with work (Aquino, Russel, Cutrona, & Altmaier, 1996; Palmore, 1982; Quinn & Berkhauser, 1994; Rife, 2001). Other older adults choose to shift careers entirely. David G., a retired engineer, has gone back to school at 68, to achieve a doctorate in computer science. He states that half his classmates are over 50.

CHANGING SOCIAL ENVIRONMENTS

In addition to these changes, there are those that a changing society brings. Children no longer grow up and bring spouses back to their parents' farm to live. The 50-year-old mother of the past was still cooking for her immediate family and often the extended one of daughters-

and sons-in-law and the children they produced. The counterpart of that woman today is working, frequently stopping for takeout on the way home, or asking family members to take care of themselves when she stays late for a meeting at the office.

Another area of drastic change not often thought about is the alteration of social interaction. Family and friends are lost through death or relocation, so that the social environment is in a new state of flux (Lysack, Neufeld, MacNeil, & Lichtenberg, 2001).

Worse than all other changes, of course, is the death of a spouse. The likelihood of death or significant illness, including clinical depression, agitation, and irritability for the surviving partner increases within the first year after such a loss. Thus, it is not uncommon to hear that a surviving spouse has become seriously ill just a few months after the loss of a husband or wife (Stroebe, Hansson, Stroebe, & Schut, 2001).

Many aspects of one's life change as one gets older, but personality normally does not (Costa & McCrae, 1980; Santor, Bagby, & Joffe, 1997). The crotchety older person is likely to have been a crotchety young person. Individuals who were outgoing and bubbly in their 20s remain that way well into their 70s. Those who were adventurous when they were young will remain adventurous as they age, as did the 69-year-old grandmother who decided to take up mountain climbing, much to the dismay of her daughter. What may change is the people's role or the way they approach life. These roles fall into three general patterns: activity; disengagement; and continuity (Covey, 1981; Cumming & Henry, 1961; Salamon, 1985a; Utz, Carr, Neese, & Wortman, 2002). Those who approach aging in the activity mode maintain an active, although often unconscious, struggle against the forces of decline, frequently struggling, perhaps even overcompensating, to be involved. The person whose mode is disengagement withdraws and accepts an inevitable decline; this withdrawal may even hasten an individual's decline, by constricting the stimulation available. The third category, continuity, is exactly what it appears to be: The person does not become more active, does not disengage, but carries on as before, both continuing and maintaining a previous lifestyle.

FRAILTIES

In addition to normal changes in emotional, psychological, and physiological systems, the average person over 65 has at least one chronic illness to cope with, the most common being arthritis and hypertension. Rates of frailty have been slowly declining (Manton & Gu, 2001). With proper care and medication, the patient is generally able to manage the activities of everyday living. *Activities of daily living* (ADL) is a clinical phrase used to describe the following basic needs: grooming, eating, bathing, toileting, dressing, and ambulating. There will be some altering of activities in a woman of 70 with a moderate case of arthritis. She may have to give up knitting or needlepoint, but she can still get around, although she may require some help. When she cannot manage the high steps of a bus, she will have to be driven by family, friends, or a car service. She will probably not be able to fasten a necklace very easily, and someone will have to help her open the jar of pickles. But, once she recognizes her limitations and learns to substitute, she will get along reasonably well.

SIGNIFICANTLY ABNORMAL CHANGES

The same cannot be said for those who experience significantly abnormal changes that necessitate the intervention of healthcare providers, such as the person who loses all ambulatory ability after a major stroke; a severely brittle diabetic who suffers visual impairment and the loss of a limb; or the aging person who loses mental capacity. All these require ongoing care and assistance. Often, this assistance cannot be properly provided by the family alone. Take the case of Gregory F., a 62-year-old who suddenly suffered a major stroke that left him paralyzed and unable to speak. His wife, Leigh, cared for him at home, feeding and bathing him, changing his adult diapers, trying to understand the needs he could not express clearly. Over a period of months, Leigh became short-tempered and frustrated. She had practically no one to provide her with the respite she needed. Although she continued to care for him, she was abrupt and harsh, never smiling. Under these conditions, Gregory, whose physical needs were attended to, suffered severely from the lack of a cheerful and positive environment.

According to National Center for Health Statistics data compiled over 20 years (U.S. NCHS, 1999), 15% of those over the age of 75 and 40% of those over 85 need help in one or more of life's basic activities and the ADLs. Turning to professionals for help in providing this type of care is often necessary and frequently better for the patient and the family. Particularly when these difficulties result in significant functional impairment and cause stress in the home, a nursing home can be superior to home care. The decision to choose a nursing home must then be made. This decision, as we see in later chapters, always engenders a great deal of conflict and guilt.

The next generation will undoubtedly see additional problems in dealing with the ailing elderly. Because women are waiting longer to start their families, it is not unusual to find first-time mothers in their late 30s and early 40s. That means they will be part of the aging population when their children are under 35 and not yet secure in their careers; if the trend continues, the children will be starting their own families at that time.

Census data trends indicate that fewer children are being born into each family unit, so the burden of caring for ailing elderly family members will fall on young people who do not have as many brothers and sisters, as in prior generations, to share the burden. And, as previously mentioned, because of an increasing life span, there will be even more elderly needing exceptional care and attention.

The problems addressed in the next chapters will be even more critical in the next generation. It is therefore imperative to understand the options for health care of the frail elderly.

Chapter **2**

Life Satisfaction and Health Care

Attitudes toward health care vary with each stage of life. Infants tend to recover quickly from the stress of a visit to the pediatrician. Adults stoically endure the necessary discomfort of the yearly physical in anticipation of a good report. The physical needs of the elderly, however, have a greater impact on the well-being of the individual. Because most illnesses in this group are chronic and can affect the overall quality of life, there is a much greater relationship between one's health and one's satisfaction with life. This chapter explores that relationship, in terms of both health and other important variables that affect satisfaction with life.

WHAT LIFE SATISFACTION IS

The term *life satisfaction* has been used in a variety of ways, to define the more general construct of subjective well-being. Included in this general construct are terms such as *morale, happiness, mood, quality of life, psychological well-being,* and *satisfaction with daily living.* A variety of definitions exist for these subordinate categories, but the term *life satisfaction* contains a more inclusive and widely accepted concept (Kane & Kane, 1981; McDowell & Newell, 1996). In general, life satisfaction is defined as a sense of well-being (Diener, 2000; Rapkin & Fisher, 1992a). It is often viewed as a buoyant and purposeful attitude, as well as an ability to deal with the challenges we face on a daily basis (Rapkin & Fischer, 1992b; Sauer & Warland, 1982).

The measurement of life satisfaction initially stemmed from a basic research need to explore both positive and negative reactions to current life situations. Life satisfaction is essentially different from personality; it is based primarily on an individual's interpersonal reactions and adaptability, rather than on underlying attitudes or traits (Carp, 1977; McDowell & Newell, 1996). Although *personality* may be defined as a complex of characteristics that distinguishes a particular individual, life satisfaction describes how an individual is likely to perceive his or her quality of life.

Measures of subjective well-being have long been found to be highly correlated with measures of mental status. In particular, the greater the degree of positive mental health, the higher the score in terms of life satisfaction and morale (Leibson et al., 1999; Morris, Wolf, & Klerman, 1975; Ware, Johnson, Davies, Avery, & Brook, 1979). It follows that a positive mental attitude in the elderly is a more significant indicator of inner satisfaction than any other. Thus, measures of life satisfaction have been appropriately used as good barometers of how aging individuals are adjusting to their life situation.

WHY THIS IS SO IMPORTANT FOR THE ELDERLY

Older adults, for the most part, are seen by the larger society as feeble, unproductive, and uninvolved. In addition, they are forced to cope with many of the changes concomitant with the aging process. It is imperative that caregivers know how individuals are dealing with these changes.

Contrary to this popular stereotype of passive and enfeebled elderly individuals, they cannot be categorized any more than can any other age group. Thus, when life satisfaction is measured, we see that each person reacts as an individual, rather than as a member of a group. Obviously, generalizations can be made in certain categories, and it is the goal of this research on life satisfaction to explore those areas of daily life that tend to cause the most pleasure and displeasure. By doing so, we illuminate, examine, and ultimately target areas of dissatisfaction, for the purpose of intervening therapeutically.

Under certain circumstances, measures of general well-being provide the best indication of those areas individuals find the most difficult (Mosher-Ashley & Barrett, 1997; O'Connor & Vallerand, 1998; Salamon & Conte, 1984). Unlike other measures of mental health, the measurement of life satisfaction does not entail the often threatening trappings of a complete psychological evaluation. Almost all measures of general well-being are simple question–answer tests that can be administered in either individual or group settings, are generally not timed, and are geared specifically to this age group. Life satisfaction measures do not take the place of psychological testing, but they do provide relevant documentation of the respondent's psychological state. As we see in the next section, many studies have found that the measurement of life satisfaction provides important data with which to target program interventions.

SIGNIFICANT FINDINGS IN LIFE SATISFACTION

Life satisfaction has been applied to determine the impact of age, health, social involvement, and marital status on the adjustment that a person has been making.

Age

By looking at very early studies and more recent research, we see that well-being in different groups can be accurately measured. In the earliest studies of life satisfaction, it was reported that, as individuals aged, their level of satisfaction decreased (Bradburn & Caplovits, 1965; Kutner, Franshel, Togo, & Langner, 1956). In a recent study of the effects of age on general well-being, scores for a group of college-age students were comparable to those of a group whose average age was 65. Although the two groups had differing responses and the tests cannot be compared on that level, the sense of well-being in each group was evidenced. A college student's pleasure is obviously not derived from the same activity that will please an older person, but each experienced a comparable sense of well-being (Lang & Heckhausen, 2001). Similarly, in a large-scale study of the quality of American life (Campbell, Converse, & Rogers, 1976), scores of younger individuals tended to be comparable to those of elderly individuals on measures of satisfaction and happiness. In an attempt to recompute the results of several studies on the quality of life and its impact on age, similar results were obtained. The underlying issues that contribute to a sense of satisfaction with adjustment may change; however, scores on measures of life satisfaction were found not to be affected by increasing age, and scores remain fairly consistent throughout (Cutler, 1979; Salamon, 1998).

Although these cross-sectional studies tend to give some enlightening results, the better measure of change with increasing age comes from following individuals longitudinally, that is, following the same group of people over the course of many years. In the first such study, a large group was followed for 25 years. The findings indicated that, in general, age as a unique variable had no impact on life satisfaction (Palmore & Kivett,

1977). At this point, most agree that there is little, if any, correlation between the two (Myers, 2000; Larson, 1978). Indeed, if it is found that an individual's level of adjustment to life is affected by age, the likelihood is that another variable, not age per se, is the causative factor.

Health

The impact of a person's health has been found to be related to the quality of life that individual reports. Three studies in the 1960s, utilizing the assessment of health made by a physician, found that, despite the age of the patient, the type of life satisfaction measure used, and the patient's health problem, there was a low but significant relationship between level of illness and level of reported well-being (Larson, 1978; Maddox & Eisdorfer, 1962; Palmore & Luikart, 1972).

These findings have been replicated in subsequent studies, but perhaps the most provocative component is the fact that self-reported levels of physical well-being are more highly related to one's level of life satisfaction than a health care professional's report (Leibson et al., 1999; George & Landerman, 1984; Willits & Crider, 1988). Examining the effects of stress and adaptation on the lives of 375 middle-class older adults, a group of researchers reached the conclusion that, although a major medical event, such as a heart attack, had the expected degree of negative effect on physical adaptation, it had no direct effect on quality of life (Palmore, Cleveland, Nowlin, Ramm, & Steigler, 1979). Indeed, in the longitudinal study referred to, subjective health (how well the individual felt physically), compared with objective health (as reported by a health care provider), was found to be the most important factor influencing life satisfaction (Okun & Stock, 1986; Palmore & Kivett, 1977).

A more detailed overview of the issue of self-reported health is in order. Many studies have found that self-reporting of illness is an accurate measure of an individual's physical state (Linn & Linn, 1980). Nevertheless, even though the correlations are strong, they are not perfect (Leibson et al., 1999). This is, in part, because patients reporting their illnesses often use lay terms and are often not given complete information on their physical health by their physicians (Special Committee on Aging, 1977). This is especially true when patients are asked to report the types of medications they are taking. Patients generally have been found to report that they take more medication than their health care providers report. Often, patients see more than one doctor and do not share this information with the physicians. Furthermore, they use over-the-counter medications that they do not readily acknowledge. Thus, a health care provider may report that an elderly patient is taking three medications, when the patient reports taking four or five. For those medications prescribed for serious and/or chronic ailments, however, there is a very high relationship between what the patient reports and what the physician reports (Salamon, 1985b).

What all this suggests is that, although health care provider reports of physical well-being are related to the patients' reported life satisfaction, how the patients view their own physical health has a greater association with life satisfaction. The patients' own views of their health are strongly related to their self-reported levels of quality of life. The more ill they see themselves, the less support they have and the poorer they view their ability to cope, the less likely they are to report high levels of life satisfaction (Krause, 1990; Lohr, Essex, & Klein, 1988).

Social Involvement

Another variable studied for its relationship to life satisfaction in the elderly is *interpersonal relationships,* alternately referred to as *social contacts, social networking, social interaction,* or *social involvement.* An early study of this variable (Rosow, 1967) concluded that individuals who reside in an environment where they can interact with their peers will experience a higher level of life satisfaction than those who do not. Subsequent studies suggested that social interaction factors are not directly related to overall levels of a sense of well-being (Lemon, Bengston, & Peterson, 1972). However, participation in broad social networks has been shown to have a desirable effect on the negatives normally associated with increasing age (Aquino et al. 1996; Pinquart & Sorensen, 2000; Myers & Diener, 1995). The personal efficiency that results from these associations brings with it a greater level of life satisfaction. Similarly, in several follow-up studies, a strong positive relationship was found between the level of social involvement and reported levels of personal adjustment (Myers, 2000).

In a study of 218 residents of a midwestern city, performed in the late 1970s, social interaction was found to be positively correlated with life satisfaction (Conner, Powers, & Bultena, 1979). In that study, *social interaction* was defined objectively as consisting of frequency of contacts, scope of interactions, content of interactions, age grading, and age exclusivity. The conclusions indicated that the number of individuals interacted with, and the frequency of contact, were not strong determinants. Instead, the *quality* of the interaction, defined as how close the individuals felt to the persons they were interacting with, was more important than any other factor in explaining the relationship to life satisfaction. This was later confirmed in other reports (Myers, 2000;

O'Connor, 1995; Willits & Crider, 1988). In a guide to counseling approaches with the elderly, Barry (1980) concluded that the quality of social interaction, rather than the quantity of individuals interacted with, is the more crucial factor to adaptability and quality of life.

In a related vein, researchers have explored the relationship between *voluntary association*, defined as membership in organizations, and life satisfaction. Here, too, several early studies reported that this form of social involvement was not related to life satisfaction (Cutler, 1973). Other early studies, however, concluded that there may be a relationship between the two, but that relationship was more directly mediated by the respondent's socioeconomic status (Edwards & Klemmack, 1973). More recent studies of individuals who were involved in activities explored the variables in more detail. Subsequently, it was found that association with an organization was not the major predictor of life satisfaction; rather, it was the level of *participation* in activities (Markides & Martin, 1979; Ward, 1979a). Similarly, involvement with religious activities seems to increase life satisfaction (Fry, 2000; Zika & Chamberlain, 1992).

The weight of the evidence strongly suggests that people who report themselves more socially involved (whether or not they objectively are) have higher levels of life satisfaction. This phenomenon of people viewing themselves in a light sometimes contrary to objective reality is not so different, whether we are talking about life satisfaction and health or life satisfaction and social involvement.

Marital Status

In one of the earliest studies conducted on the subject, single people over 60 reported approximately the same level of well-being as their married counterparts (Kutner et al., 1956). In the case of most widowed, divorced, or separated persons in the same age group, a lower level of well-being is reported. Holahan (1981) also indicated that married women had higher levels of life satisfaction than their unmarried peers, even if the unmarrieds were successful in other aspects of life. Several other studies, performed at different times and using different measures of well-being and life satisfaction, have found similar results (Hendrick & Hendrick [reviews]); there is a slight but significant positive relationship between being married and life satisfaction. Attempts to explain this suggest that the lower levels of life satisfaction experienced by most widows can be ameliorated by a confidant, thus reducing loneliness and offering companionship (Hendrick & Hendrick, 1997).

Older adults who remain single all their lives show a higher level of life satisfaction in the 25–49-year-old category. However, increasing age causes this level of satisfaction to reverse, in part because of the normal declines associated with aging (Ward, 1979b). This change may be socially induced: As a person ages and associations are formed with older people, the single lifestyle receives lower rates of social support. There is also some indication that, for women, just being married is strongly associated with higher life satisfaction, but men have higher life satisfaction if they are married and report an active sex life (Matthias, Lubben, Atchison, & Schweitzer, 1997).

Recent studies have reportedly identified what appears to be a U-shaped curve of life satisfaction across the marital years (Gilford, 1984; Salamon, 1988). If this is true, it would indicate that life satisfaction is highest in the earlier years, experiences a decline in midlife, and increases as the couple enters the senior years. This may result from the strains that accompany parenting and careers, which are highest during the middle phases of a marriage. Although this seems to contradict the often-expressed "empty-nest" syndrome, it does suggest that individuals who have invested a great deal of effort and energy in their relationship will derive more pleasure and support, and will report that they are more satisfied in their later years.

Generally speaking, we may conclude that married people have a higher level of life satisfaction in their later years than their unmarried counterparts.

Socioeconomic Status

As in all age groups, socioeconomic status (SES) has a marked bearing on a person's sense of satisfaction with life in general. Levels of education, occupation, and income are generally accepted as the three primary factors that make up the construct of SES; as the three factors increase, SES increases. And as SES increases, so does the likelihood of a concomitant increase in satisfaction with life.

There is some confusion about the precise effect socioeconomic status has on life satisfaction. Some have suggested that it is the primary determinant of quality of life (Myers, 2000). Others have suggested that, although SES is an important contributing factor to quality of life, the effect is not nearly as strong as other variables, such as health. Still others have found that SES acts as a moderating variable, affecting the effects of other factors related to life satisfaction. For example, older people of lower socioeconomic status tend to rate their health as worse than those with the equivalent illness at higher levels of SES (Pinquart & Sorensen, 2000). In addition, "relative deprivation"—the way people view their status in relation to others—is an important factor in determining an individual's life satisfaction. Most research suggests that older adults view their SES in a utilitarian fashion. If they have enough money to help their children (Stevens, 1992) or they can manage their financial obligations comfortably (Gray, Ventis, & Hayslip, 1972), they are satisfied. If an individual is feeling a sense of deprivation relative to others, his level of life satisfaction is affected.

There seems to be little doubt that life satisfaction and SES are intertwined. The precise strength of the relationship and whether the relationship is a direct one are yet to be proven (Csikszentmihalyi, 1999; Myers, 2000).

CONCLUSION

Clearly, many factors in one's life combine to create life satisfaction: health, social involvement, marital status, and socioeconomic status. Much research effort has gone into the study of this highly important aspect of aging, and, although not yet perfected, recent tools to measure the components that make up life satisfaction have been developed. The next two chapters explore the settings in which health care is provided to frail elders. In **Chapter 5,** we report on research that examines the degree of life satisfaction experienced by individuals in these diverse settings.

Chapter 3

An Overview of Health Care Environments

Most people consider only two methods of caring for ailing elderly: home or nursing home. Yet there is a wide range of options from which individuals may choose their form of care. The choice is a highly individual matter, because what is desirable for one person may not be desirable for another. As shown in later chapters, several important factors must be taken into account when the decision must be made.

The six major health care alternatives are reviewed in this chapter, and case histories help to illustrate the strengths and weaknesses of each health care environment.

PRIVATE PHYSICIANS

The trusted family physician has long been an essential part of our ongoing health care, yet older adults, who visit doctors more than any other age group (National Center for Health Statistics [NCHS b & c], 1982), often find they can no longer turn to their family doctor. The doctor, having aged along with the patient, may retire just when the patient needs medical care more than ever before, or the older person may have relocated, cutting off all direct contact with that trusted physician. In cases in which doctor and patient have not moved or retired, a change can take place because of family pressure. The elderly patient's adult children, seeing younger physicians, may note the difference in doctors' approaches and urge their loved one to seek medical assistance elsewhere. This is not surprising: There is evidence that some older doctors may not be keeping abreast of new developments (Kovar, 1980), and few physicians have received training in geriatric medicine. In fact, the trend seems to be improving, but only about 10% of the medical schools in the United States teach geriatric medicine as a specialty (Association of American Medical Colleges, 1999). In addition, the use of specialists increases with the age of the patient. Older people, who are twice as likely as younger individuals to have chronic conditions (Schneider & Brody, 1983), see internists more frequently, and have more medical tests performed, than younger individuals (NCHS, 1982a). Older adults tend to visit office-based physicians, on average, six times per year, and younger age groups visit fewer than three times per year (NCHS, 1978, 1982a; Krauss, Machlin, & Kass, 1999).

For the older patient, a visit to the doctor's office is not always looked upon as a necessary nuisance, as is often the case in almost all other age groups. The elderly person may see the office visit as a social activity, talking to others in the waiting room or engaging the receptionist or nurse in conversation (Salamon & Nichol, 1982). Although the middle-aged people in the doctor's waiting room are constantly looking at their watches, the older patients may be so busy socializing with others in the waiting room that they do not bother to notice who goes in or when.

Of course, receiving one's health care in a private physician's office depends on the patient's ability to get there, which in turn usually implies that the patient is well enough to live on their own in a community setting. It also suggests that the patient can afford the doctor's fees, or that the doctor accepts the patient's insurance coverage.

OUTPATIENT CLINICS

The cost of visiting a private physician may be out of reach for the individual whose doctor will not accept the schedule of fees detailed by medical insurance. The patient must pay the doctor's higher fee out of pocket. Even in those cases in which a doctor has agreed to accept Medicare payments, it is up to the patient to pay 20% of the doctor's fee, because Medicare takes care of only 80%. For this reason, and because many individuals do not have their own doctors, outpatient clinics and hospital emergency rooms tend to become the places where older people receive much of their medical care. The care received in these settings is quite adequate. Although some patients may not like seeing a different doctor on subsequent visits, there is a beneficial side to that practice.

Anita K. was an elderly woman who was "tired of living." At 85, she sounded quite reasonable when she said with much conviction that she saw nothing much left for her: "I'll only get older and sicker," she said. She was seen by an elderly psychiatrist at the outpatient clinic, who later reported to the woman's daughter that there was nothing wrong with her mother. "She makes sense," he said. "I really can't blame her. But you'd better keep an eye on her, so she doesn't harm herself."

The next time Anita went to the clinic, another doctor, a much younger psychiatrist, saw her. He did not agree with the previous psychiatrist's assessment that she was simply too old to live anymore. He recognized her depression and started to treat it actively with a combination of medication and referral for psychotherapy. Less than two months later, Anita was a "new person," with her old zest for living. At a family party, she was heard to say that it was good to be alive, and her family now knew that her previous wish to be done with life had been her depression talking and not "herself." If she had been seeing only one doctor, a doctor who did not treat her depression, Anita's final years would have been lived in a state of despair.

In the same way, many doctors still miss depression and call it dementia, or even an inevitable consequence of aging. Mrs. G., 68, confused and disoriented, was taken by her family to the emergency room of a local hospital. The attending physician determined that it was not an emergency situation and directed her to the medical clinic. The doctors there told the family that Mrs. G. was suffering from dementia and that little could be done for her. Subsequently the family made a follow-up appointment, at which time she was seen by another physician, who ordered a battery of tests, physical and psychological. The results indicated that Mrs. G. was suffering from an acute confusional state brought on by an underlying depression and poor nutrition.

Unfortunately, there are unscrupulous individuals who take advantage of the elderly patient's situation. They accept Medicare and Medicaid as payment in full, without asking for additional fees, not even the 20% they are required by law to collect from the patient. Although the care they give is not inferior, they compensate for the lower income per patient by ordering many more tests and further consultations with other physicians in their group. To correct these injustices would require a complete reevaluation of the medical insurance reimbursement scheme (Butler, Grossman, & Oberlink, 1999; Lubitz, 1995).

Clinics tend to see patients who reside in the community, as well as those who reside in institutional settings. Often, patients who cannot ambulate on their own are transported to these settings in ambulettes.

HOSPITALS

Although most people know that a hospital is a place for acutely ill people, few understand the dynamics of the hospital today. People were once not discharged until significantly improved or their illness was determined to be chronic, but the guidelines for hospital care are more complex today, especially in this time of managed care. For example, Adele R. was admitted to the hospital following an occurrence of fainting. She was found to need a heart valve replacement, and surgery was scheduled almost immediately. During the procedure, coronary bypass surgery was also performed. The artery needed for the surgery was taken from her leg. According to government guidelines, Adele was entitled to spend seven days recuperating in the hospital. On the seventh day, despite her complaining of pain in her leg where the artery was removed, she was discharged. Two days later, at home and in pain with a fever of 102°F, she called her surgeon. He told her to take two aspirin and call him later. She took the aspirin, but, instead of calling the doctor again, she went to the emergency room. The resident physician took a look at her leg and immediately admitted her to the hospital. She had developed an infection that had to be aggressively treated.

The reason Adele was not kept in the hospital originally, in spite of her complaints, is that the hospital was acting under the guidelines of Medicare's Prospective Payment System, based on Diagnostic Related Groups (DRGs). Under this reimbursement scheme, designed to keep health care costs down, hospitals are reimbursed for Medicare costs based upon the patient's illness category, rather than on the illness itself. There are 470 DRGs, which reflect the average cost for care of a particular group of illnesses. This system has been used by the federal government since 1983 and became effective nationwide in January 1988. As Smith said in the *New York Times* (Smith, *New York Times,* 3 April 1988), "When hospitals are paid by the day, the longer the patient stayed, the more the hospital was paid. Under the DRG system, the sooner the patient leaves, the more the hospital earns." And managed care companies are even more stringent.

Therefore, Adele's first hospitalization allowed only seven days of recuperation. Had she remained in the hospital under that category beyond seven days, all additional costs would have been borne by the hospital. When she was readmitted, it was under a different category. Of course, had the infection been more obvious to the attending physician, her category would have been revised, and she would have been allowed to remain for further treatment, but the initial pressure of diagnosis and reimbursement is difficult to overlook. Before the advent of the DRG ratings, a patient like Adele, complaining of discomfort, would probably have been advised to remain in the hospital for additional observation.

The DRG rating is not as arbitrary as it may seem. It was brought about by the fact that both medical and hospital costs have skyrocketed, particularly among the elderly, who use hospitals twice as often as other age groups and are perhaps encouraged by their families to stay in the hospital longer than necessary. In fact, as a general rule, those over the age of 65 tend to stay in hospitals twice as long as younger age groups (Krauss et al., 1999), not always because of the greater seriousness of their ailments, but often because of the slower rate of recovery. It has been determined that much of this recovery time can and should take place in other environments, freeing hospital beds for acutely ill persons in any age group.

The use of hospitals by the elderly has been analyzed and certain patterns have emerged (NCHS, 1999): Older men are hospitalized more frequently than older women; the poorer elderly and minorities are hospitalized almost as frequently as the more affluent and nonminority elderly; there are more hospital stays now than before, attributable to the advent of Medicare and Medicaid.

Although most patients, including the elderly, receive proper treatment in hospitals, there is a difference in attitude in the voluntary or not-for-profit hospital and the private hospital, when it comes to dealing with the elderly. Private hospitals sometimes employ the "emergency room hustle" (Butler, 1975); that is, after a cursory examination, the patient is told that the complaint is consistent with the aging process and is sent home (Strange, Chen, & Sanders, 1992). In cases in which hospitals admit elderly patients who rely solely on Medicare to pay their hospital bills, the hospital will often play the "transfer game," sending these patients to public hospitals (Butler, 1975). The hospitals are trying to keep their beds for private, paying patients. Transfer of adult Medicare patients to public hospitals is not as common as it once was, but it still occurs.

These issues, primarily relating to reimbursement and the proper provision of care, have led to a further exacerbation of the problems in hospitals. There is a growing backlog of "alternate level of care" patients—elderly people who no longer need the acute care services provided by the hospital, but who must receive ongoing care and remain in the hospital because they have no other place to go for this care. The hospital may not discharge them until proper services can be arranged, either at home or in a nursing home. Hospitals with these alternate-level-of-care patients tend to be penalized by being reimbursed at a lower rate, but the overhead remains the same. Furthermore, hospital staff have begun to refer to such patients as "dispos" or "NHPs" (nursing home placements), which means that they are awaiting disposition to a nursing home. With the acute care needs of other patients, the staff simply does not have enough time to attend to the individuals classified as alternate level of care.

After elderly patients are discharged from the hospital, they often require continued medical supervision and care. There are a variety of settings in which this type of follow-up care can be provided. Depending on the needs of the individual, care may be provided in an assisted living facility (also known as an intermediate-care facility), a skilled-nursing facility (which is a nursing home), or at home.

HOME HEALTH CARE

Depending on the needs of the individual, there are a variety of options for health care in the home. These can be grouped into two general categories: support with activities of daily living and professional services. The former provides social home care, usually under the auspices of area agencies on aging, which are private nonprofit programs created by the Older Americans Act of 1965 (see **Chapter 9**). Numbering about 670 throughout the United States, these agencies receive most of their funds from the federal government. The programs provide nonmedical services such as homemaking, assistance with meals, and other chores, as well as social service assistance, including case management, information, and referral. These agencies do not require physician supervision, but are prevented from providing any form of medical or nursing care.

Professional services, on the other hand, do provide home-based medical care. These services are provided by certified home health care agencies. These agencies may be private and nonprofit (such as visiting nurse associations), proprietary, or public. Funding for these services is provided by Medicare and Medicaid. Certified agencies provide active medical and rehabilitation programs, including skilled nursing, physical therapy, or speech and occupational therapy, as well as consultation with social workers, psychologists, nutritionists, et cetera (Bishop, Kerwin, & Wallack, 1999).

Although there are no exact figures on how many individuals are serviced by home care agencies, it has been estimated that as many as 2.5 million people in the United States would benefit from home health care. Medicaid expenditures for home health care increased from $7 billion in 1994 to over $12 billion in 1997 (Health Care Financing Administration [HCFA], 1999).

Agnes T. was hospitalized for hip surgery following a fall. When she was discharged from the hospital, she needed physical rehabilitation and a registered nurse to change the dressings on the wound, which was healing very slowly. The hospital discharge planner, in conjunction with Agnes's daughter, made arrangements for Agnes to be discharged to her daughter's home, where the daughter would provide ancillary support. In addition, the local visiting nurse service would attend to the professional needs. A physical therapist came daily and the nurse came three times a week. In this case, Agnes's care was both appropriate and satisfactory.

The mandate of home health care agencies is to prevent or delay institutionalization, but many studies over the years have questioned whether these agencies have been efficacious (Beland, 1986; Capitman, 1986; Morrow-Howell, 1998). Indeed, one study concluded that five major home care programs reviewed were not effective in substantially altering patterns of institutional use (Capitman, 1986). For the past three decades, it has been believed that the frail elderly prefer home care services to being institutionalized, but it would appear that this may not always be the case. No consistent government guidelines exist by which home care is evaluated, so comparisons to care in other settings are not reliable (Welch, Wennberg, & Welch, 1996).

There have been some documented cases in which home care is not only inappropriate, but results in tragic consequences. Instances of elder abuse, in which children abuse their frail parents, appear to occur more frequently in situations in which children care for parents at home (Steinmetz, 1988). Although not very common, elder abuse takes place more frequently than expected.

Many people certainly benefit from home health care, but there is evidence that many of these ailing elderly do not benefit and are ultimately placed in a nursing home (Penrod, Kane, Finch, & Kane, 1998). There is also evidence that, in many cases, these patients do better in the nursing home environment.

ASSISTED LIVING

As a result of the demands of an increasing population of older adults and rapidly rising health care costs, a new level of care has been introduced and is rapidly expanding. Assisted living, which began only in the past decade (Hawes & Phillips, 2000), is now estimated to serve more than 600,000 older adults in more than 25,000 to 30,000 facilities (Citro

& Hermanson, 1999). These numbers vary so greatly because some definitions of an assisted living facility include continuing care retirement communities and very small board-and-care facilities.

In the past, individuals who required some medical care, but who were not sufficiently frail to need a skilled nursing home, would have the options of getting care in an intermediate care facility or health-related facility. Those facilities would offer services, but also have a medical model-of-care program. Health-related facilities no longer exist. They appear to have been replaced by assisted living programs.

The key philosophy of an assisted living program is to enable the residents to live in a homelike environment (Assisted Living Quality Coalition, 1998). Assisted living programs typically have a housekeeping staff, serve at least two meals per day, offer recreational programs, and have some form of 24-hour supervision. Residents live in small apartments, by themselves or with others. These apartments often have a small, functioning kitchen. Standards for care and availability of services vary greatly from one assisted living program to another. Indeed, defining which programs are to be considered as assisted living facilities is difficult. Standards vary from state to state, as do the types of services offered (Hawes & Phillips, 2000). Some states require that assisted living facilities provide apartments with kitchens. Some states allow daily nursing care to be offered; others do not. Essentially, the question of definition remains: Is an assisted living facility a medical program, and therefore, under the auspices of a state's department of health; or is it a program to be regulated under the standards of board-and-care facilities? Regardless, assisted living programs are clearly filling a growing need.

Lillian R., a 78-year-old woman with severe arthritis, needed help with transferring herself. She had difficulty getting out of her bed or into and out of a shower. Her husband had passed away two years earlier and although she enjoyed the apartment she had lived in for the last 20 years, most of the friends and neighbors she had in the neighborhood had moved away. Lillian did not need intensive medical care, just occasional assistance. What she really needed was some help with meals and getting around in an environment tailored to her needs, and social programs. Together with her children, Lillian chose an assisted living facility that offered her the opportunity for meals, recreational activities, and help getting around. What really helped her decide was the fact that her own little apartment at the facility had a sitting area and a small kitchen.

At least one study has shown that the primary reason that some people choose assisted living is that it offers a continuum of care, should the need arise (Krout, Moen, Oggins, Holmes, & Bowen, 2000). Other studies have found that the transition to an assisted living site enhances quality of life by increasing social participation and family involvement (Erickson, Dempster-McCain, Whitlow, & Moen, 2000; Mitchell & Kemp, 2000).

NURSING HOMES AND SKILLED NURSING FACILITIES

There were approximately 1.5 million nursing home beds in the United States in the 1980s (Sirocco, 1985). At that time, it was estimated that additional beds would be necessary in just a few years. As of 1998, there were 1,834,000 nursing home beds (AHCA, 1999).

Most nursing homes are relatively small, averaging about 80 beds. About 65% of all nursing homes are private for-profit facilities, and about 25% are private nonprofit institutions sponsored by ethnic, religious, service, or fraternal organizations. Fifty-six percent of nursing homes are either owned or operated by large corporate chains (Harrington, Carillo, Thollaug, Summers, & Wellin, 2002). The remaining nursing homes are public facilities (Harrington, Swan, Bedney, Carillo, & Struder, 1996).

At any given time, only about 5% of those over the age of 65 reside in a skilled nursing facility (Schaie & Geiwitz, 1982), a number that has remained relatively stable. However, it has been estimated that individuals over the age of 65 run a 50% risk of spending some time in a nursing home. Slightly more than 1% of the population between the ages of 65 and 74 are institutionalized; the percentage rises to almost 7% between ages 75 and 84. The percentage more than triples in those over 85: About 22% of that age group reside in nursing home institutions.

Nursing home care has been described as one of the most costly forms of health care available. It has been estimated that over $30 billion was spent on institutional care in 1982. Approximately half this amount was paid from personal resources (Gilson, Waldo, & Levit, 1983; Special Committee on Aging, 1986). By 1999, that figure rose to $90 billion (Heffler et al., 2001). These figures are extremely high, but they reflect a variety of legitimate and unavoidable expenses. A good portion of the cost of care in nursing homes is a result of what has been referred to as "hotel fees," which include the cost of food, rent, and utilities, or basic overhead. These costs should be considered inevitable, regardless of where the person resides. Nevertheless, to help keep costs down, most states now use a reimbursement mechanism similar to the DRGs used in hospital settings. This system, referred to as resource utilization groups (RUGs), provides reimbursement to the facility according to a patient's need for nursing care, rather than according to specific illness. For example, a person who has suffered a stroke and is left with some paralysis on

one side of the body will be categorized as requiring physical rehabilitation. Otherwise, nursing supervision is minimal. On the other hand, a
person who has suffered a stroke but is left with a behavioral problem
and tends to wander, requires more nursing supervision. Technically, the
illness is the same, but the level of care is obviously quite different.

The RUG system has been faulted as arbitrary and favoring a select
group of patients. Some patients, including those suffering from a dementia or emphysema—individuals who are in need of sophisticated health
care—often do not meet the RUG requirements for care in a nursing
home (French, 1988). The need for sophisticated health care does not
necessarily imply more intense or expensive care. Thus, patients who
have ailments which require extensive staff intervention are more likely
to be admitted if facilities are allowed to charge more for their care.

The typical nursing home resident is an 85-year-old widow, although
about 22% of nursing home residents were never married; 5% are divorced;
and only about 10% have a living spouse. About half of the residents in a
nursing home have no relatives, and more than 60% have no visitors on
a regular basis (AHCA, 1999).

When nursing home residents have a spouse residing at home, the
prognosis for discharge from the nursing home to one's home or to a
lower-care facility is far better than for those in other groups. But even
then, only 20% will return home. The majority of nursing home residents are not discharged, living out their days there, or they die in hospitals to which they have been transferred from the SNF. Functional
disability of nursing home residents increased over the last two decades,
from roughly 70% to almost 85% (George, 1984; Danger, 2002).

Despite the bad publicity nursing homes have received over the years,
they are not necessarily dumping grounds for old people. Nursing
homes serve a very important need and, in many cases, are far superior in
atmosphere and supervision to what is pictured in most people's minds.

In **Chapter 9,** we list several Web sites that rank nursing homes:
Among them is the Center for Medicare and Medicaid Services. Ranking
is based on a variety of factors, but, because of the methodology used to
rank a facility, the results may be confusing and misleading. It is therefore important to check more than one Web site and, when possible, to
visit the nursing homes you are considering.

Irma B., an 84-year-old widow, was in the hospital for emphysema.
While there, she suffered a mild heart attack. She also had a recent hip
fracture and was in need of rehabilitation. When she was discharged
from the hospital, the doctors recommended nursing home placement,
but Irma's daughter took her mother home to live with her family. Irma
felt isolated in a home filled with teenagers and busy adults, with nobody

near her own age. After some discussion, they decided to explore the possibilities of nursing home placement. At a few nursing homes, they put Irma's name down on the waiting list, and, in a few days, a bed was available at one of the homes. Irma had a difficult adjustment for the first two weeks, but she made friends and took part in regular recreational and social activities. While at her daughter's, Irma had watched television alone; at the nursing home, she sat with others like herself and watching became a social event, rather than a lonely and isolated pastime.

Virtually all nursing homes are required to comply with both federal and state laws that regulate the quality of care they provide (Public Health, 42 CFR Pt 483). These laws cover proper staffing, documentation, programming, nutrition, medical, and therapeutic treatments, provided in a protective environment. The question of whether or not nursing facilities meet their goals, and even whether there is an accurate technique to assess that, remains open-ended (Walshe & Harrington, 2002). Several studies report that increasing regulation has brought about improvement in nursing homes over recent decades. Similarly, some reports recommend increased funding to enhance the ability of nursing homes to provide better services (Wunderlich & Kohler, 2001). In general, facilities that view themselves as providing innovative programs are more likely to provide higher quality of care (Castle, 2001).

Choosing the best facility is not an easy task, especially because there is a shortage of nursing home beds. As a result, many individuals often see home health care as the only viable option.

CONCLUSION

Frail older people are presently estimated at 12.8 million (NCHS, 1999) and their numbers are projected to continue to rise with the aging of the baby boom generation. This group needs some form of health care. Although we have discussed a number of options in this chapter, the number of health care choices for the very frail elderly are limited. Realistically, there are only two: Reside in one's home or with a close relative, seeking individualized home health care; or move to a skilled nursing facility. The next chapter focuses on these two options in more detail.

Chapter 4

Examining the Home Care—Nursing Home Choice: Bias and Reality

There is a distinct prejudice against nursing homes, in great part because of bad publicity, sometimes earned, often not. In many cases, it comes down to a question of attitude—the attitude of the people placing the elderly in a nursing home and the attitude the elderly perceive as a result. The "poor mother had to go to a nursing home" viewpoint is transferred to all concerned and thus becomes a self-fulfilling prophecy.

Most people feel that the older person is better off at home, and that a nursing home should be considered only when home care is totally impossible, as illustrated in the following case.

For a long time, Fred R., 75, had been supplying the physical and emotional support needed by his frail 91-year-old sister, but it had become increasingly more difficult for him to continue. Her son and daughter, with families of their own, lived far from their mother and could not provide daily help. Clearly, she belonged in a nursing home, where her needs could be provided for, but Fred had grown up believing that only those with no living relatives should be sent to "such a place." Fred resented the fact that her children were not taking their mother to live in one of their homes. It was possible that they could not do so for many reasons, but Fred would not consider any of them. To him, a mother should not be sent to a nursing home, no matter what the circumstances, no matter what the "excuse."

MOTIVATIONS FOR CHOOSING HOME HEALTH CARE

There are a number of reasons why older individuals and their families choose the home health care option. One is the obvious *fear of institutionalization* and the stigma attached to residing in an institution. This fear has some basis in fact, but is blown out of proportion because of the stigma of social deviance attached to many forms of institutional confinement. Prisons, mental institutions, hospital back wards, drug rehabilitation centers, and nursing homes are often grouped together in people's minds as places for individuals who cannot live in a normal social milieu. The individuals residing in these settings are therefore viewed as needing to be kept away from healthy society.

The *familiarity* of the home environment and the sense of independence derived from this familiarity, as well as the fear of institutionalization, are obvious reasons for the frail elderly person to choose to remain at home.

Arthur G., 81, had lived in his own house for 52 years. His children grew up there; his wife died there. Lately, the house had grown seedy, but Arthur did not seem to notice the rusty rings in the bathtub or the cracked shingles on the outer walls or the peeling paint in his bedroom. He saw his house as the same palatial one he had envisioned it to be when he first took out the mortgage as a young man. Even more important, he knew every creak and every crack in the place. Before he became too frail to do so, he could walk through the rooms late at night with no lights on and never miss a step, even at his advanced years. He dreaded giving up this comfortable "old shoe" and going to a place where even the bed would be strange and new.

The desire to stay in familiar surroundings often overrides a more sensible choice, becoming the main focus of the decision-making process, regardless of the problems involved. In addition, the sense of warmth and caring one receives from loved ones is, in the minds of many elderly, far superior to any care one might expect from strangers, although this is not necessarily the case (Haug, 1985; Montauk, 1998).

Often, there is also the mistaken belief that home care is far less expensive than nursing home care. However, when you consider that most of the costs of caring for an individual at home, with the exception of medical and support services, must be absorbed by the family, the cost becomes much greater. Increased costs may also include the lost wages of the primary caregiver and transportation to medical care. Even special diets can be expensive (Montauk, 1998; Chappell, 1994; Rimmer, 1998).

With these fears and desires, elderly persons may avoid seeing themselves as a burden when choosing home care, but the daughters or

daughters-in-law, on whom the burden usually falls, may see it quite dif-
ferently. It can mean the end of their independence at a time when they
are becoming free of the demands of young children. The ailing parents
may see the family only as a unit and are therefore unable to recognize
that they are upsetting the family environment (Brody, 1984; Haug,
1985; Rimmer, 1998).

Margaret took care of her mother at home for as long as possible, but,
when the severely ailing elderly woman needed 24-hr care, Margaret
reluctantly placed her mother in a nursing home. She reports that her
mother is getting full-body massages, her feet are rubbed three times a
day, and her food is being pureed. Margaret said,

> "The different nurses try to see who can get her to eat the most.
> When Mom first arrived, she was eating about 5% of her meals.
> One of the nurses bribed her with a pumpkin cookie and chocolate
> muffin and got her to eat 75%.
>
> When I go now, I can just enjoy Mom. No more running home
> after work and stuffing sheets and stuff into the washer. No more
> straining my back washing and rolling her. This is divine.
>
> Of course, she's still not speaking to me. I went over there
> tonight, and she refused to say anything but hi, until I got up
> ready to leave. Then she said, 'See you later.' So I know she can
> talk, just not to me. But I know she is in the right place. I can live
> with my decision."

Previous generations believed in the *continuity* of family life, and the
ongoing transfer of tradition and emotional interdependence within that
unit. It is not surprising, then, to find that many elderly do not want to
break this chain and that there are many families who respect this family devotion.

Reciprocity—giving to others the equivalent of what has been received
from them—often plays a part, even if subconsciously, in the minds of
all family members choosing to accept or provide home care. The patient
and the children remember the years when the issue of caring was
reversed, when the parent was the caregiver. As a result, the child feels
responsibility to return care when the parent is in need, and the parent
develops the expectation that care will be provided (Brody, Johnsen,
Fulconer, & Lang 1983; Horowitz & Shindelman, 1983).

Ann R. had a unique way of handling a situation with her mother
when she decided not to place her in a nursing home. She says, "As you
know, I never did put my Mom in an Alzheimer's home. She died in her
own home, thinking she was living completely independently. I had

three women on the payroll, watching over her, visiting, seeing that she ate and dressed, and she thought they were just friends. It pays to lie. If she'd known they were hired, she'd have fired them in a heartbeat."

Guilt, sometimes stemming from a sense of not having done enough, often plays a major role in choosing to have a parent stay at home. This, combined with the younger generation's fear of the parent's aging process, may motivate the children to become the primary care providers. Although this behavior is seen by outsiders solely as a burden to the caregiver, there is a psychological benefit—the care provider is gaining a sense of emotional fulfillment by rising to the occasion and overcoming fear of the parent's deterioration.

These six reasons for choosing care in the home—fear of institutionalization, familiar surroundings, costs, continuity of generations, reciprocity, and guilt—form the basis of the decision making process for many families. There are also highly individual reasons, but some or all of these six are usually taken into consideration. Furthermore, it must be made clear that, when nursing home care is considered inappropriate, it is not necessarily because the services provided are in any way inferior to those available at home.

WHEN HOME CARE IS IMPOSSIBLE

A variety of studies have identified the determinants of placement in nursing homes. Most studies, performed from the perspective of the patient's orientation, have found that several factors are helpful in predicting who might ultimately reside in a long-term facility. These factors include advancing age, difficulty in performing the ADLs, mental confusion and disorientation, and limited social contacts (Finlayson, 2002).

When the matter is viewed from the perspective of the potential home care provider, several other variables come into play. The most pervasive consequence of providing care in the home is the strain, both physical and psychological, not only for the primary caregiver, but for the entire family (Rimer, 1998; Zarit, 1996). The degree of stress varies from family to family, but it can also change on a daily basis in a single family unit. There are days when the caregiver feels overwhelmed by the responsibility, while other family members are making demands of their own upon her. The kindergarten-age child comes home with a note from her teacher announcing that the child needs a costume to be a flower in the school play the next day (the child forgot to tell her mother the previous week). The older child pleads with her mother to be a class mother. "All the mothers take turns," she wails. Add to that a husband who may be bringing home a customer for dinner, and it is easy to see what washing, feeding, and toileting a parent adds to the burden of an already stressed individual. When the caregiver recognizes that the demands placed upon her exceed her ability to meet them, she begins to understand that home care may no longer be possible.

Another factor is the large number of dual-career families. More and more women work outside of the home, and the majority are believed to do so for monetary needs, rather than for career fulfillment. Thus, it can be a financial hardship for a daughter or daughter-in-law to give up the added income and stay home to provide care for an elderly parent. Despite that, many elderly parents expect daughters, much more frequently than sons, to care for them (Stone, Cafferata, & Sangl, 1987; Zarit & Whitlack, 1992).

When there are poor family relationships, it is unlikely that home care would be a wise choice. Tensions will be greatly magnified by the additional stress placed on all family members. Ailing parents will also suffer from these conflicts and will be dealing with tensions outside of the conditions that have confined them. The mother and daughter who have never agreed on anything will not suddenly become amenable and companionable when the mother is in need of care. As a matter of fact, the mother, becoming dependent on the daughter at this stage in her life, will probably add tension and resentment to this conflict.

The current generation, having delayed childbearing until the middle or late 30s or even the early 40s, will have an additional problem in the future. Their children will be considerably younger when they are older than in preceding generations. The 55-year-old woman may have a 15- or 16-year-old with accompanying teenage problems, when her own mother is 73 and needing her daughter's care. In fact, this problem exists today. Furthermore, the percentage of women waiting to have children until they are in their 30s is expected to increase significantly in the next generation (Stone, Cafferata, & Sangl, 1987). When a teenage son, already somewhat rebellious and having to deal with the pressures of his age, must give up his bedroom (a room he has viewed as his sanctuary for many years) to his ailing grandfather, it is not unlikely that the conflicts and ill feelings he experiences will stay with him well into his adult life (Pruchno, Peters, & Burant, 1995; Shifren, 2001).

Although an extra room may be available, other facilities in the home may be inadequate. The bathroom may be too far away from the patient's bedroom or may require climbing a few steps. A child's room, filled with commotion, music, childhood games, and ensuing arguments, may be too close to that room. In the case of a somewhat ambulatory patient, stairs must be taken into consideration. Will it be possible for the patient to climb stairs or get around, or will she be isolated, not because of her illness, but by her location in the house?

Even when the foregoing situations are not a factor, it is still possible that home care may be the wrong choice. When the needs of the elderly parent are extreme and the care required is beyond the competence of a nonprofessional, it would be unwise and impractical to attempt to provide home care. In any event, such care would probably be inadequate. This is a particularly pressing situation when the ailing parent is suffering from both a physical illness and a dementia (Chenoweth & Spencer, 1986; Pratt, Schmall, & Wright, 1987; Pushkar, Feldman, Morkiewicz, & Andres, 1995). Adult children providing home care for these individuals experience inordinate levels of stress and frustration, frequently becoming ill themselves, and ultimately, in most cases, they are forced to consider placement in a nursing home.

EMOTIONAL BARRIERS TO THE NURSING HOME CHOICE

The Family's Feelings of Guilt

Decisions regarding placement in nursing homes are rarely made by patients themselves. Instead, children and other family members are forced to recognize that they can no longer provide adequate care. Although it was originally believed that it was usually a daughter or daughter-in-law who was called upon to provide a major portion of physical and emotional support, and that they suffered the most guilt, because it was an admission that they were unwilling or unable to continue (Kahana & Kahana, 1985), it is also clear that, in many instances, sons contribute almost equally (Kaye, 1997). Guilt is an emotion that causes us to feel uneasy because we believe we have not acted in a responsible or appropriate fashion; on the other hand, when we have acted in a way that is inappropriate, guilt is also clearly manifested.

Many individuals have developed an overwhelming sense of guilt because they feel that they cannot provide for their parents as their parents provided for them. In most cases, however, it is impossible to do so. Aside from the societal pressures that are often the result of two-career families and the needs of their own children, it would be unwise for them to reject the professional assistance available to them from well-trained care providers.

Guilt can sometimes drive us to behave in ways that better judgment would avoid as in the following example. Dorothy's mother was in a nursing home, and Dorothy felt compelled to visit her every day. The compulsion was so great that Dorothy stated that she could not live with herself if she did not make daily visits. One winter day, during a fierce snowstorm that made driving treacherous, Dorothy drove to the nursing home, skidding several times. When she finally arrived, shaken from the ordeal of the trip, she found her mother warm, comfortable, and well cared for, with Dorothy not fully aware that her behavior was motivated by something other than the desire to see her mother. A significant portion of the motivation that drove her to compulsively visit her mother was guilt.

Guilt can cause a variety of psychological and physical problems (Cantor, 1983; Fransella & Dalton, 1990), including depression, anxiety, frustration, helplessness, sleeplessness, lowered morale, isolation, and interference with lifestyle in social and recreational activities. Physical stresses include lowered energy levels and the onset of chronic ailments. As a result of the guilt, the caregiver also denies her own needs. Thus, she will forgo many of her own requirements, in order to care for the needs of the ailing parent. This is sometimes taken beyond the parent's needs, with the caregiver often doing more than is necessary. This is motivated, once again, by guilt and can result in the care provider feeling completely alone in the driven need to provide care.

Ambivalent, hostile, and immature feelings toward an elderly, frail parent are not uncommon among adult children. However, it must be acknowledged that a child who deals with a parent from guilt may not be able to provide the type of assistance the parent may need (Salamon, 1987). Guilt, in most cases, is unwarranted, because there are instances when the child simply cannot take on or maintain the intensive care of an ill parent.

THE ELDER'S REACTION TO THE MOVE

Relocation is considered to be one of the most stressful events in life. When families move from one home to another, they leave behind many memories, a familiarity with the environment, and often a large network of friends. There is the fearful anticipation of gaining a welcome in the new place, getting to know the unfamiliar surroundings, and becoming comfortable in the new location.

The move to a nursing home includes all of these concerns and fears. It means separating from friends and family, and may also mean a loss of a feeling of control over one's life. Adapting to someone else's routines and regulations can be difficult and depressing at any age, and moreso in the later years, after one has established lifelong habits and patterns. The woman who has eaten a half–grapefruit for breakfast every morning for 45 or 60 years will not be happy without this small pleasure, which has actually become a necessity, in her view.

Over the years, it has been suggested that relocation results in *transfer trauma*, which was hypothesized to cause increases in mortality and morbidity. Simply stated, the fear was that, if older individuals were moved from one environment to another, even to a much better environment, they would suffer sufficient distress to increase their illnesses and even shorten their lives. However, reviews of transferred elderly patients suggest that relocation is not as serious a problem as previously thought. Transferring a patient can provoke anxiety in the patient, but the moves are not necessarily traumatic; they do not lead to increases in mortality and morbidity. Furthermore, if the individual is prepared for the transfer, the anxiety experienced is significantly reduced (Borup & Young, 1982).

Adjustment disorders can occur. *Adjustment disorders* are emotional reactions to changes in one's life. In many cases, these reactions may occur with the transfer to a new environment. Although not as serious as formerly believed, these conditions do exist and should be recognized for what they are—usually minor upsets in the life of the patient. Patients experiencing adjustment disorders are often able to overcome the anxiety in a relatively brief period, after which the individual accepts the new routines. Staff members provide the support by showing patients around, familiarizing them with all aspects of the home, and introducing them to other residents. At the same time, other residents provide evidence that people in nursing homes are not isolated and that one's impairments are not unique. There is some comfort in the fact that others are frail, yet are managing in this setting. Indeed, friendships are formed, and social activities and relationships may be maintained. Adjustment disorders can also occur in reaction to an illness or physical impairment. Thus, it is important to determine whether the disorder is a reaction to the transfer or to an ailment, or a combination of both.

Although making the final decision regarding care for an ailing elderly family member is a highly individual process, much can be learned from the experiences of others. As we have seen in this chapter, there are many reasons why home health care is often selected as the primary choice. Yet, in many instances, this choice may be inappropriate for the family, as well as for the ailing person. It is a choice that should not be made without careful consideration of all aspects of the problem.

Chapter **5**

Which Health Care Setting is Best for Frail Elders?

There has been much debate about the most appropriate setting for the ailing elderly. Earlier studies suggested that the funding of home health care services is the most appropriate method of dealing with this problem (Kramer, Shaughnessy, & Pettigrew, 1985). Other studies questioned these findings and indicated that care of the ailing elderly is best provided in a nursing home setting (Chappell, 1994; Rimer, 1998). This chapter describes an ongoing study whose purpose was to explore the degree of life satisfaction experienced by the aging population in various health care situations.

HOW LIFE SATISFACTION IS MEASURED

As we have seen in **Chapter 2,** life satisfaction is an important indicator of general well-being, particularly among elders. Over the past few decades, a number of scales have been devised to assess the quality of life of older adults. Perhaps the first scale to measure subjective well-being in the elderly was the Cavan Attitude Inventory (Cavan, Burges, Havighurst, & Goldhammer, 1949). This inventory was designed to measure the respondent's attitude in eight areas of personal functioning: health; friendship; work; finances; religion; usefulness; happiness; and family. The statistical validity of the scale was never formally established, but it was reported that its overall reliability was fair to good. Nevertheless, the Cavan Attitude Inventory has not been used extensively in recent years, because it is difficult to administer, and scoring is very complex (McDowell & Newell, 1996; Kane & Kane, 1981). A briefer scale—the Kutner Morale Scale—was initially designed for telephone administration. It fell out of favor because it was found that the questions were primarily measures of confidence, rather than of life satisfaction (George, 1979).

Two scales designed by Neugarten, Havighurst, and Tobin (1961) remain among the most widely employed measures of life satisfaction in use today. The Life Satisfaction Index A (LSIA) and Life Satisfaction Index B (LSIB) were created to assess the degree of successful aging in a large sample of older adults in Kansas City, MO. The initial construct of life satisfaction was defined by these researchers as comprising five categories: zest; resolution and fortitude; congruence between desired and achieved goals; positive self-concept; and positive mood. Although these areas are supported by clinical observation and interview (Savage, 1975), psychometric studies of these five categories, as independent factors, do not hold up (Liang, 1984). However, three of the dimensions—mood, tone, zest, and congruence—do seem to be statistically observed most frequently (Adams, 1969). There is good reason to believe that the domain of life satisfaction encompasses a larger number of sub–areas than those suggested by Neugarten and her group (Conte & Salamon, 1982).

Another frequently used scale, the Philadelphia Geriatric Center Morale Scale (Lawton, 1972), is comprised of six dimensions: surgency (activity); acceptance of status quo; easygoing optimism; attitude toward own aging; agitation; and lonely dissatisfaction. Reviews of the psychometric properties of this measure suggest that attitude toward one's own aging, along with agitation and lonely dissatisfaction, are the only factors that tend to be reproducible (Lawton, 1975; Liang & Bollen, 1983; Morris & Sherwood, 1975).

The question of statistical appropriateness has plagued some of these measures, but there is little question about the importance of the concept of life satisfaction. Indeed, in an attempt to resolve the question of which quality of life scale to use, Lohmann (1977) gave the Cavan Scale, Kutner Morale Scale, the LSIA, and the Philadelphia Geriatric Scale to a group of 259 elderly Tennesseans and found that all of the measures were significantly correlated. What this suggests is that all of the scales have a high level of concurrent validity and, to a certain degree, are measuring much the same construct.

To investigate life satisfaction properly requires that the measure itself be designed to represent the entire domain (Okun, 1987). The Life

Satisfaction in the Elderly Scale (LSES) (Salamon & Conte, 1984), now known as the Life Satisfaction Scale (LSS) (Salamon & Conte, 1998), is designed to do just that: measure the quality of life in the aged, in a variety of settings. Furthermore, it incorporates the largest domain of items that have been empirically shown to form the general construct. Eight categories make up the LSS (formerly LSES): daily activities; regarding life as meaningful; goals; mood; self-concept; health; finances; and perceived satisfaction with number and quality of social contacts. The LSES has been validated and tested for its reliability in a variety of settings (Salamon & Conte, 1984, 1998; Salamon, 1988). This scale goes a long way toward providing us with a means to reliably assess the quality of life in older adults.

The research that follows goes beyond prejudices and helps to answer the question of whether home care is always preferable. To measure accurately the question of life satisfaction, as it relates to the environment where health care is provided, the LSES and LSS were chosen as the measure of quality of life, because it is sensitive to small changes in a variety of subareas that contribute to well-being (Salamon & Conte, 1984, 1998). The major hypothesis of the study was that there would be a difference in life satisfaction scores, based upon the different settings in which the elderly received health care (Salamon, 1987).

HOW THE STUDY WAS CONDUCTED

In the initial study, adults of both sexes, aged 60 and above, were drawn from a variety of health care settings. Study participants were chosen from two hospitals, two clinics, four health-related or intermediate care facilities, three nursing homes, and the private practices of three community-based physicians. Homebound elderly, who received care from visiting nurse services, were also invited to participate in the study. In subsequent studies (Salamon & Conte, 1998), participants were drawn from two assisted living centers, two additional nursing homes, and home care.

With the approval of the facility—or, in the nonfacility settings, of the primary health care provider—participants were randomly selected from available lists or from those who happened to be in attendance on a randomly selected date (this selection process is known as a sample-of-convenience study). The individuals selected were approached by research staff and asked to take part in the study. Those who agreed were asked to answer the questions as honestly and accurately as possible and were assured that there were no right or wrong responses. It was explained that the survey was a measure of their feelings. Participants were further informed that the questionnaire did not measure ability and did not affect the care they would be receiving. Confidentiality was assured, although the patients understood that their physical conditions would be discussed with their doctors, but only for the purpose of the study.

When necessary, the researcher or research assistant helped patients complete the questionnaires, but did not interpret any of the questions. Where help was needed, the staff read questions and response options exactly as they were written, then checked off the responses given by the participants.

Some interviews were conducted on a one-to-one basis; others were handled in groups of various sizes. In the larger groups, patients were at widely spaced desks or tables, with research assistants walking around to provide assistance. Regardless of the method of interview, there were no apparent differences in the respondents' attitude toward the study or in their abilities to comprehend the procedure.

RESULTS OF THE STUDY

Analysis of the results of the initial study indicated equivalent response rates across the varying survey methods. The average time for completion of the questionnaire was 20–30 min. Furthermore, an analysis of the overall response rate indicated that, regardless of the setting, at least 80% of all the individuals who were approached to take part in the study completed the entire process. Overall, a total of 294 individuals were approached to take part in the study, and 241 completed the entire process.

An analysis of the demographic makeup of the participants, compared to the population of the United States at large, indicated that, overall, the sample was statistically similar. However, those in this study reported slightly higher rates of single marital status, lower-status occupations, and lower incomes. These differences may be the result of an inappropriate selection factor, because those elderly requiring long-term health care tend to show this pattern of income, occupation, and marital status.

Although participants were able to check a box on the form asking for summary results of the study, less than 1% did so. However, in the nursing homes, health-related facilities, and clinic settings, the researcher was often asked by the medical director or senior administrator to give a follow-up lecture. These lectures were attended by most of the participants and a good number of staff members. This was also the case in the follow-up study performed at the two assisted living facilities.

The interviewing, analysis of data, and summary of results was an ongoing process that lasted almost a year. The bulk of the findings confirmed previous results of life satisfaction, in relation to the variables discussed in **Chapter 4.** There was no correlation between age and quality of life, but patients' perception of their own health status, as well as how socially involved they were, was related to their reported levels of well-being. Those who were married reported higher levels of life satisfaction than did single patients; those who reported themselves as being active had slightly higher life satisfaction.

There were no surprises here. However, one startling finding emerged when levels of life satisfaction were compared across the six health care settings. In all the subcategories of the LSES, except achievement, people receiving care at home attained the lowest life satisfaction scores.

Table 5.1 lists the average scores in all categories of life satisfaction for each of the health care settings. Those in intermediate care facilities or in nursing homes were among the highest in all eight categories, *with those residing in nursing homes having the highest average overall scores.* The LSES measures eight subcategories of quality of life. In all, the scores were either highest or among the highest for both facility care settings. Even when severity of illness was controlled for by matching and comparing the degree of illness in each health care setting, the findings stood up (Salamon, 1987). These findings indicated that people in nursing homes have higher levels of life satisfaction, and were more satisfied with their lives, than were people receiving health care in other settings. And those receiving health care at home had the lowest levels of satisfaction.

TABLE 5.1   Average Scores of LSES per Health Care Setting

	Senior Center	MD's Office	HRF	SNF	Hospital	Home Care
Total LSS	132.269	132.967	136.787	138.200	133.250	118.237
Routine	16.750	16.023	18.127	17.028	16.600	12.474
Meaning	16.808	17.581	18.383	17.475	16.775	14.526
Achievement	15.692	16.465	16.170	17.200	15.875	16.947
Mood	17.578	18.139	18.447	18.330	17.500	16.263
Self-concept	17.289	17.535	17.638	16.950	17.260	15.526
Health	13.481	12.465	13.872	15.825	13.875	11.211
Income	15.923	15.302	14.681	16.200	15.800	14.459
Social contact	18.769	19.465	19.468	19.225	19.575	18.211

Three other smaller studies looked at levels of life satisfaction of the aged in health care settings. In one study (Robinson, 1983), it was found that those receiving home care had excessively low morale. In the other two studies (Schwirian, 1982; "What's New," 1984), the researchers were surprised to find that residents of nursing homes had unexpectedly high levels of life satisfaction. These results, as well as the findings of this study, demand that the long-held belief that there is nothing as good as home care be reevaluated. The follow-up study, which included the assisted living sites, employing the LSS, resulted in virtually the same findings. Those in assisting living and nursing homes scored consistently higher on life satisfaction than those receiving home care. Those residing in nursing homes achieved an average total LSS score of 139.120, those in assisted living averaged 141.730, and those receiving home care averaged 119.000. Another study, comparing 158 residents of nursing homes and assisted living facilities, found no difference in health outcome, including functioning, health, and levels of depression, between the two sites (Pruchno & Rose, 2000).

BENEFITS OF NURSING HOMES

Because the results were initially so unexpected, and because the concept of choosing nursing home care over home care is contrary to what many of us believe, it is important to look again at the benefits that may be derived from nursing homes and assisted living facilities. Why did people in nursing home and assisted living facilities report higher levels of life satisfaction?

Although it would seem that people being cared for at home have the benefit of enjoying surroundings that are familiar and comfortable, in many cases, they nevertheless feel isolated—an ill person in a family of active members. If the primary caregiver is a relative, that person will have other obligations and responsibilities. If a professional is hired as the primary caregiver, the number of hours spent with the patient is generally limited, and the relationship may be distant. Even when the worker is personally involved and proficient, the patient is interacting with only one person. In nursing homes, the numbers of people—both patients and staff—who make up the complete environment allow for more socialization and more opportunity to interact; relationships can be developed and maintained, the patient belonging to a "larger family" (Cutillo-Schmitter, Zisselman, & Woldow, 1999; Salamon & Nichol, 1982).

The homebound patient with very little social or therapeutic stimulation may often just sit and watch television for hours, dragging from one meal to the next. Nursing homes, however, must comply with regulations that require them to maintain and post activity schedules, with a staff dedicated to encouraging patients to participate. The nursing home or assisted living residents still have the option of watching television alone if they choose, but viewing can also be done in a group. And even watching television can be a form of social activity. It is certainly more fun sharing a laugh at *I Love Lucy* or *The Love Boat* reruns than laughing alone. Even when the facility residents are arguing over what program to watch, they are interacting. Research has shown, time and again, that recreation and socialization activities help elderly individuals overcome loneliness and depression, and moderate the effects of stress (Kaplan, Campbell, & Gore, 1977; Mosher-Ashley & Barrett, 1997).

Other activities, directed to every level of physical ability, range from sitting on a stool painting a picture (as Lillian W., 84, did, with results that surprised herself, as well as the activity director), to getting out in the fresh air for a group stroll, to piling into buses for a shopping trip. And it is no longer unusual to see wheelchair-bound patients shopping at a mall. These social trips are quite different from the plight of the homebound elderly, who must be taken out by a family member, who may do so grudgingly or may not have the equipment to transport a wheelchair.

In addition, many nursing home residents discover hidden talents when they first take up a paintbrush or knitting needles, learn to play canasta, bridge, or produce items that will ultimately sell in the gift shop. These individuals feel a deep sense of pride in their new accomplishments, which obviously leads to a heightened degree of satisfaction with their lives.

When it comes to medical care, the 24 hours of supervision available in all nursing homes and some assisted living facilities may be viewed as unarguably superior to taking an elderly patient to a doctor's office or waiting for the doctor to get to the house. No matter how well-equipped you make the home with hospital beds, commodes, and tray tables, it is still second-best to a facility designed with medical infirmities in mind. In fact, living at home and seeing all these supportive aids around may be more depressing, because the home is drastically changed, with daily reminders that one needs help. Two issues are related to this factor. First and most important, there is little doubt that people can be inappropriately cared for at home, if residing at home deprives them of the care normally offered in an institution setting (Howell, Proctor, & Rosario, 2001). Second, physical limitations tend to threaten self-esteem, especially for those residing among others who are not impaired. Once an individual resides in a setting such as a nursing home, and is among others with similar ailments, his own limitations may not seem as severe, and hence there is less threat to self-esteem (Myles, 1970).

One of the arguments against placing elders in a nursing home, even when it becomes necessary, is the fear that the ailing family member will not adjust to the new environment. There is little scientific reason to believe that the aged cannot adapt to a new setting.

Jack S. relates a story about his great-aunt Shirley. "She lived in Queens, New York, for the past 50 years and is now 99 years old. She was diagnosed with severe arthritis in her spine 18 years ago. Her hearing and vision are excellent and her mind is as sharp as ever. She had a live-in aide in her second-floor apartment for the past 16 years. The aide was an immigrant and was paid cash. Aunt Shirley went through a series of people. The longest tenure for anyone was 9 years. There were always problems and various family members always had to visit to ensure she was receiving the proper care. She rarely went outside, because of the stairs. We tried for years to admit her to a nursing home, but she always refused. Approximately 9 months ago, her physical condition deteriorated enough that we were forced to admit her to a nursing home. I recently visited her, and it was the happiest I have seen her in 10 years. She looks forward to waking up every day and participating in all the activities the nursing home schedules each day. The social interaction with the other residents brightens her day and makes her realize what she missed terribly over all these past years. Her life has been enriched since entering the nursing home."

Several studies of transfer trauma have found that, if individuals being transferred understand the reason for the move, they will not react negatively or suffer significant adverse consequences. In fact, once older persons understand the need for a more supportive environment, they are likely to feel less comfortable at home. For the older adult who has difficulty understanding that the transfer is necessary, hearing it explained often and with sensitivity will ultimately make it acceptable.

Certainly, people should take treasured possessions when moving to a nursing home or to an assisted living facility, more for the emotional value than for utility. One 90-year-old woman had her antique hat-stand—or costumer, as it was called in her day—standing in the corner of her room, to hold the coats she seldom needed because she was usually confined. The room's closet could have held the coats, but the lady liked to see them hanging on her familiar costumer. And the staff of the facility, understanding the important memory value of the piece, used it to stimulate discussions with her.

The nursing home offers an additional boost to subjective well-being not found at home. When ill or frail people are alone, with little activity to occupy them and no one with whom they can compare themselves, their own illnesses seem much worse. They focus on their aches and pains, and see little to be thankful for. It is not uncommon, on the other hand, to hear patients in a nursing home, or residents in assisted living facilities, say, "Well, I'm sick, but not as sick as my roommate. We help each other out," or, "Oh, that's a good program for those old people,"—the speaker of 79 not counting herself in the group of "old people."

Given these comparisons, the findings of the study begin to make more sense. Indeed, if one takes into account the basic environmental differences between facilities and private homes, it is not surprising to see that nursing homes and assisted living programs may actually contribute to an individual's sense of well-being. Home health care is certainly appropriate for many types of health care, but patients who require long-term medical supervision and ongoing rehabilitation for functional disabilities may do best in an environment designed more specifically to meet their needs.

In a follow-up to the original life satisfaction study, ten newly admitted nursing home patients were followed for a period of six months. On average, the patients were assessed by an intake team one month prior to their admission to the home. Given their ages and infirmities, it was expected that they would continue their rapid decline in both physical and psychological health. This was not so in seven of the ten cases. All of these seven patients showed signs of improvement—slight, it is true—but any improvement in their level of functioning (which slows the anticipated decline) is an unexpected and extremely positive sign.

One woman, suffering the ravages of Alzheimer's disease at home, could not dress herself and could not recognize her daughters or her caregiver. When she walked, she would try to run away from home and would even have occasional violent outbursts. Out of sheer frustration, the daughters decided on nursing home placement. Their guilt rapidly diminished when, after just one week at the home, their mother began dressing herself again, even putting on makeup. Although she still could not remember her daughters' names, she was able to tell them accurately about the "social" she had attended the previous evening, and of her new "boyfriend."

Another woman had been cared for at home by a succession of professionals, each of whom she summarily dismissed as incompetent or uncaring. In addition to her physical impairment, being wheelchair-bound as a result of a stroke, she was labeled as "paranoid." This label was assigned because her behavior toward the caregivers was fearful, rude, and obnoxious. No longer able to find professional help, the family opted for a nursing home. Once there, the woman did not have a single outburst and did not display paranoid behavior. When approached about it, the patient responded, "I'm here to be cared for. At home it was painful. They were intruders. Here they are part of my family." Although most patients do not articulate their feelings quite this well, many feel the same way.

Still another woman, one of the 7 in this study who improved, played the piano for the first time in 15 years. Formerly a moderately well-known concert pianist, she no longer played at home, because her fingers had begun to deform slightly from arthritis and following the mild stroke that caused some memory impairment. In the nursing home, she played every Tuesday evening, to the delight of staff, patients, and—most important—herself.

There may even be some reason to believe that there is a correlation between life satisfaction and longevity. In a small study of nursing home residents and those in home care who were followed for several years, those with higher levels of life satisfaction were found to live longer (Salamon & Conte, 1998). Also in a group of 129 intermediate care nursing home residents followed for 4 years, the strongest predictor of survival was found to be positive satisfaction with life (O'Conner & Vallerand, 1998).

The decision to place an individual in a nursing home, however, is never an easy one. Not all patients improve there. Some, upon admission, may show an emotional adjustment disorder, in which they act and appear anxious and depressed. Over time, and with the proper intervention, adjustment disorders tend to dissipate. Still, exploring the option of nursing home placement is difficult. But, as later chapters show, there are guidelines to use and procedures to follow. Selecting the most appropriate type of care is essential for the well-being of the ailing person and for all those who will be physically and emotionally responsible for ongoing care.

Chapter 6

After Nursing Home Placement: What Elders and Their Families Report

To explore satisfaction with life as it relates to the health care setting further, 80 individuals in 6 nursing homes and 2 assisted living facilities, as well as several family members, were interviewed. Patients were chosen as a sample of convenience. They also fit the following criteria: They were all able to communicate verbally; and, although they may have been suffering from a dementia, they were still oriented to their surroundings and could participate in the interview process.

The interviews were conducted by a professional who was not a member of the patient's health care team. The technique of using an outside interviewer was selected as a means of reducing the fears patients might have about revealing their true feelings regarding the facility and staff to whose care they were entrusted. The nursing home patients could be fearful that staff members might retaliate if the patients spoke critically of the staff and that the reactions of the staff could affect the care they received.

PATIENT RESPONSES

The patients were asked essentially one question: How do you like it here? The interview was open-ended; participants' responses could be as lengthy as they wished. If the interviewer felt that the response was abbreviated and that the individual really had more to say, the interviewer encouraged a lengthier discussion. Responses were taken down verbatim, then coded by two other researchers, regarding satisfaction, dissatisfaction, or ambivalence with the care being received and with the nursing home environment. Interrater reliability was constantly checked and found to be .94 or better, indicating virtually no disagreement in interpretation of the responses made by the patients.

One study (Kahana, 1975) found that, of 50 patients interviewed in 14 nursing homes, about 30% considered their care and surroundings to be moderately good to very positive; 27% were neutral about how satisfied they were in the nursing home; and 34% expressed negative reactions to life in a nursing home. Overall, those results suggest that many of the patients interviewed for that study reported average to excellent satisfaction with the nursing home environment. In this survey, a higher percentage of the nursing home residents reported satisfaction with the care they were receiving and with the nursing home environment. No one was happy or satisfied with the illness or disability that created the need for nursing home care, but 65% reported that they received good care, had made new friends, learned new hobbies, and were generally very satisfied with life in the nursing home. Only 16% reported outright dissatisfaction with the nursing home setting; 19% responded ambivalently, indicating that their feelings about the nursing home or assisted living facility were neutral, neither satisfied nor dissatisfied.

The following comments, taken verbatim from taped conversations, indicate the range of responses. The first group was coded as "satisfied":

Single female, 76: "I did make the right decision in coming here. I get more care here than anyplace else."

Widowed female, 67: "I had no choice. This is it. . . . I made the right decision."

Widowed female, 82: "Where would I be otherwise? I had no one to take care of me . . . I can't complain about the care. They treat me well."

Married male, 83, residing with wife: "I'm here because my wife needs the attention very badly. I think it's advisable that I stay here with her through the last few years. . . . It's reasonably good care. I would say it's more on the good side than the bad. . . . Yeah, I would say I made the right decision for both of us."

Single female, 69: "Many ill and discouraged people feel that a nursing home is the last drop-off before the grave. Death can come at any time and anywhere. I consider my nursing home a happy home, for home is where the heart is."

The next few quotations reflect responses coded "ambivalent":

Widowed male, 90: "I'm here because I have no other alternative. I've been in Florida for many years, and it was just too far for my son to travel. . . . As far as my son's concerned, I made the right decision. As far as I'm concerned, I'm not sure."

Widowed male, 82: "It's no different here than at home. There care is the same. I don't know if it's good or bad being here."

Of those who responded "negatively," many simply said, "I just don't like it here." Few of the respondents elaborated on that reaction, but one did:

Widowed female, 77: "My daughter made the decision. As far as she's concerned, she did the right thing for herself. . . . If it was up to me, I'd rather be in my own apartment with a private nurse. . . . Sometimes these patients who aren't normal come into my room. I have no privacy."

The decision to choose a nursing home is not usually made by the patient alone. When handled properly, the trauma of the move is minimized, and the relationships among the patient, the family, and the patient's caregivers can be enhanced. The following anecdote illustrates just how this is accomplished. The anecdote was taken from one of the patients whose response to the survey was coded "positive."

Marie, a divorced female of 81, was living in her own senior residence apartment; she prepared her own breakfast, but went to the in-house cafeteria for lunch and dinner. When she became ill with heart failure, her children ordered a nurse to stay with her during the day, and the nurse brought Marie all her meals from the cafeteria.

Although Marie's condition improved enough for her to go to the cafeteria for meals, the nurse found it less bothersome to bring the food in than to get Marie out. It was easy for Marie to accept this lazy way of life, but, as the days went on, she became more dependent on her nurse and withdrew from being the outgoing, friendly person she was known to be.

Marie subsequently needed bladder surgery, and her bladder burst during the operation. There was now no question about it: Marie needed nursing home care, and, although she protested and cried the day she was transferred from the hospital to the nursing home, it was not long before she was once again having her meals with others like herself. Unlike the private nurse, the nurses in the nursing home encouraged her to get dressed, helped her to the dining room, and helped her around the other activity rooms (library, gift shop, sewing room).

Not too long after, Marie sent her son a card in which she wrote, "Good news. I love it here." To her daughters, she said, "I eat with nine other people at a round table, and you should hear how they bicker sometimes [said with a certain degree of enjoyment]. I told them here I must have my cranberry juice every day, and it's always right there at my place."

During one visit with her daughter, Marie urged her to go with her to the gift shop. "I want you to see what my tablemate knitted. Can you imagine! They're actually going to sell it." This last was said with a twinkle in her eye and in her voice, indicating that maybe she too could produce something worth selling.

REACTIONS OF FAMILY MEMBERS

In addition to the 80 nursing home and assisted living residents who were surveyed, 48 family members were asked to respond to a similar question posed by the survey team. These individuals were selected in part because of their availability and their interest in family discussions at the facility where their relative lived. The question to them was: Can you please give us your impression of this facility? Their responses were coded in the same fashion as the patients' responses. Of the 48 people responding, 43, or 90% were positive. Families' reactions, however, included statements regarding their own frustration with providing patient care at home. This was especially true for those family members caring at home for patients suffering from dementia.

No effort was made to determine the patient's degree of cognitive or physical impairment, and the impression of the patients having dementia was based on the family member's report, but the findings were not surprising. Several studies over the years have indicated that family caregivers have difficulty tending to individuals whose illnesses make them so demanding (Haley, Levine, Brown, & Bartolucci, 1987; Pagel, Becker, & Coppel, 1985). Several additional studies have shown that certain types of the care provided, types of illnesses the older person suffers from, or the age of the family member, all have variable effects on the caregiver's well-being (Hooker, Manoogian-O'Dell, Monahan, Frazier, & Shifren, 2000; Shifren, 2001; Tornatore & Grant, 2002). Thus, although most responses from family members were positive, the responses may also reflect the fact that transferring the patient to the nursing home resulted in a diminution of levels of frustration and possible guilt, anxiety, and depression, which could have resulted from being unable to care for one's elder at home. They may also reflect a desire not to say anything negative about the facility, although an attempt was made to control for this bias: The interviewers were not staff members or care providers. The following anecdotes represent family members' reactions.

The 87-year-old widower had lived with his daughter and son-in-law for two years. During that time, his condition deteriorated until he became forgetful and started to have difficulty caring for himself. He was always asking, "What should I do now?" His caregiver takes up the story:

"Whenever he asked, 'What should I do now?' a little bell went off inside of me. The anger grew. His first question in the morning, 'What should I do now?' his last question at night. I would say, 'Now it is time to get dressed,' but that was not enough. He needed specific instructions: 'Now it is time to put on your shirt. Now it is time to button the buttons.' I tried not to say it in anger, but it became harder and harder. It was almost impossible getting out to work in the mornings. Then he started giving the home attendants a hard time. They were trained to handle his questions, but they, and we too, had a hard time convincing him that they belonged with him and were not there to hurt him and were not stealing from us. It just became too much.

"We decided to explore the nursing home option, and at first it was a difficult choice. We spoke with Dad about it, and he seemed to understand. When we had finally chosen the two best places, we took him to see them. He was not happy about it, but he did not reject it either. In fact, he said, 'If it has to be, I want this one,' indicating which of the two places he preferred. Getting him in was not easy. It took several weeks before they even called us to tell us that our papers were all in and in order. Once he was accepted, though, almost overnight he was a changed person. He does not ask that question anymore. He goes to activities. He is not easy on the nurses, but they don't seem to mind. And we can finally visit and not worry about him or get angry at him. This place is great for him and us."

Sam was in his mid-80s when his wife entered a nursing home. Sam lived alone and kept to himself most of the time. After three years of living alone, Sam could no longer take care of himself, and his children discovered that he was not eating. They felt that Sam should be in the nursing home with his wife, but it was actually other residents of the home who urged Sam to enter, and he went willingly. Sam's wife has since passed away, and Sam, now 92, is still enjoying a great deal of affection and attention. His son reports: "My father was not used to being around so many people, and at first he stayed in his room and read. But he blossomed in the home and is enjoying the many activities. It's a pleasure seeing my father so happy. There was a time, just a few years ago, when I thought it was all over for him. Instead, he now studies religion and history in classes given by a local college.

His son also illustrated his father's revitalized sense of humor, repeating a story in his father's own words: "I got into the elevator, and there were two nurse's aides there. One grabs me and hugs me, so I put my head on her bosom. And she said, 'You like that, Sam, don't you?' and I said, "It's better than horseback riding."

Both of the previous anecdotes illustrate not just the respite value of the nursing home setting for the family caregiver, but also the importance of the support provided to the elderly in this type of setting. In the first case, the structured atmosphere of the home, as well as the staff's ability to deal with the patient's cognitive losses on a professional level contributed to the patient's peace of mind. In the second case, being in an environment where the residents' needs were met and where the opportunity for socialization was encouraged, led to the enhancement of the patient's quality of life, allowing him to remain active and involved, rather than alone and isolated.

HOME CARE NURSES

To add a degree of confirmation to the findings of the study reported in **Chapter 5,** as well as to those above, 12 home care nurses were interviewed. These nurses worked full-time for three home health care agencies. Their responsibilities included an average caseload of 50 patients, whom they visited at least once a month. The nurses provided supervision to the home health aides and practical nurses, who spent more time with the elderly patients. On occasion, they also provided direct care. In those instances, they saw the patient at least once, usually twice, per week.

The purpose of the interview was to ascertain the professional's impressions of the patients, the type of care they were receiving, and the home setting in general. The interviews were open-ended, unstructured, and, because of the constraint of having to deal with working professionals, generally time-limited. They averaged no more than 10 min, but in one case, an interview lasted an hour. Given the anecdotal nature of this survey, the results can be considered tentative at best. Indeed, this was just the first step in a pilot study of nurses who provide care to the elderly in a variety of settings.

In almost every case, the conclusion that the 12 professionals drew from dealing with ailing elderly in their own homes was that the majority of the patients they were seeing at home, about 65%, were lonely and isolated. The nurses also stated that, in most instances, these patients were not receiving the best form of care, which was available in other settings.

Some of the nurses who were clearly committed to the concept of providing health care at home were quick to point out that home health care provided the benefit of familiar surroundings and a strong sense of independence. One nurse in particular said that, should she ever need this type of care, she would prefer to receive it at home. "I won't get the constant attention," she said, "but at least I'll have more control over my life." Another of the nurses said that, given the same set of circumstances, she would prefer a good nursing home. "I was always a very social person, and I need that type of setting. Besides, in an institution, there's always someone around to help if you need it."

CONCLUSION

This chapter presents the results of three surveys: elderly patients residing in nursing home or intermediate health care settings; family members of individuals living in a nursing home; and home health care nurses. None of these surveys, taken individually, can be considered highly scientific. They are all highly impressionistic and anecdotal. But because the reports from the three disparate viewpoints tend to converge, some conclusions, albeit tentative, may be drawn. Certainly, no one is comfortable with the illnesses that necessitate the need to seek out long-term care, either at home or in a nursing home. But, for those already involved in providing care, the nursing home setting seems to be a highly viable and, in many cases, the preferable option. Again, the points that tend to stand out are that the nursing home setting provides constant care in an environment where social isolation is unlikely.

These studies indicate that it is inappropriate to approach the nursing home option with the popularly conceived negative point of view. When long-term care is needed, it is beneficial for all concerned to adopt a positive point of view. As we have seen in **Chapter 3,** there can be strong emotional reactions even to considering a nursing home. But, as we have also seen, there are instances when home health care may be impossible and inappropriate.

In the next chapter, we explore the process of making the decision, choosing a facility, and easing the transition.

Chapter 7

The Home or Nursing Home Quiz

Over the past few decades, the field of gerontology has seen the development of several questionnaires to help students and the general public understand, recognize, and debunk the myths associated with the aging process. Among these are Facts on Aging Quizzes I and II (Palmore, 1977, 1980, 1981), which provide an important educational service. For families with a frail elder, it is often important to have an awareness of the pragmatic issues of the provision of care. This chapter increases our awareness of these issues through the use of a quiz. It covers all phases of caring for an elderly loved one and allows the respondent to gain a broader perspective of the situation. Following the quiz is a question-by-question explanation and analysis of responses.

The following quiz is designed to be taken by a family member who is the potential caregiver. It is based upon real-life needs that must be considered. The quiz can be used by a professional to help clients decide whether they are good candidates for providing home care.

For all questions that do not apply, score 0; otherwise, score yourself according to the number indicated next to the answer you select.

1. Does the home or apartment have an extra room with easy access to a bathroom?

    _____ yes(0) _____ no(1)

2. Can you afford the additional expense for providing care that is not covered by insurance (food, linen, etc.)?

    _____ yes(0) _____ no(1)

3. Is a responsible adult available to watch the patient at home?

      _____ yes(0) _____ no(1)

4. Do all adults in the family have to work outside the home?

      _____ yes(1) _____ no(0)

5. If yes, will there be a responsible family member available to supervise care at home?

      _____ yes(0) _____ no(1)

6. Is there someone to relieve the primary family caregiver?

      _____ yes(0) _____ no(1)

7. Are there young children at home who require supervision?

      _____ yes(1) _____ no(0)

8. Are there teenage children at home?

      _____ yes(1) _____ no(0)

9. If there are, how will they feel about limiting their activities (friends dropping in, loud music, etc.)?

      If you do not anticipate a problem, (0) _____
      If you foresee conflict arising, (1) _____

10. Do you have the emotional stability to deal with old people or sick people?

      _____ yes(0) _____ no(1)

11. Do you, yourself, fear the aging process?

      _____ yes(2) _____ not sure(1) _____ no(0)

12. Did you have a difficult time dealing with your mother or father?

      _____ yes(1) _____ no(0)

13. If yes, were these issues ever resolved?

      _____ yes(0) _____ no(1)

14. Is there a basic personality clash between you and your parent?

_____ yes(1) _____ no(0)

15. How would you feel about providing care for your parent?

_____ very uncomfortable(4) _____ somewhat uncomfort-able(3) _____ not sure(2)_____ would not bother me(1) _____ very comfortable(0)

16. How would you feel if you had to feed your parents or change their diapers?

_____ could never do it(4) _____ don't think I could do it(3) _____ not sure(2) _____ would not bother me(1) _____ com-fortable(0)

17. Will the patient require a variety of rehabilitation programs, such as physical therapy, occupational therapy, speech therapy?

_____ yes(1) _____ no(0)

18. If yes, are these programs available through home care services?

_____ yes(0) _____ no(1)

19. Is home health care available in your community?

_____ yes(1) _____ no(0)

20. If it is available, are there long waiting lists and limitations on the type or extent of care provided?

_____ yes(1) _____ no(0)

21. Has the patient always been a social individual?

_____ yes(0) _____ no(1)

22. If yes, are there options for a variety of social activities at home?

_____ yes(0) _____ no(1)

Now that you have answered all the questions, add up the point value of each answer to determine your total score.

Your total score: _____

If your total score is 10 or under, you are a good candidate for providing home care.

If you scored 11 to 20, your ability to handle home care is questionable.

A score of 21 or over indicates that you should explore nursing home
care for your elderly relative.

Before you draw any conclusions, please read the following comments
relating to each question as numbered in the quiz. If you find that understanding the reasoning behind a question prompts you to change your
previous response, please do so, and make a note of your revised total.

1. *Does the home or apartment have an extra room with easy access
to a bathroom?* Privacy is important, not just for the patient, but also for
the rest of the family. Frail individuals often need special equipment,
such as hospital beds, tray tables, commodes, or wheelchairs. It is vital
to have a room that can accommodate such equipment, and although it
may not seem essential for a bedridden patient to be near the bathroom,
think of the caregiver emptying bedpans and carrying water back and
forth for bedbaths.

2. *Can you afford the additional expense for providing care that is not
covered by insurance (food, linen, etc.)?* Home care expenses pile up
rather quickly. Medicare pays most of the cost of specialized health and
therapy services, but there is a time limit on reimbursement and a limit
on how much it will pay. Therefore, chronic, long-term illnesses may not
be covered by Medicare, even under the catastrophic health insurance
guidelines. As discussed in **Chapter 8,** Medicaid pays for health care only
for the financially destitute. If ailing elderly persons live in a nursing
home and their financial resources have dipped to the minimum specified
by the government, Medicaid assumes financial responsibility. Unless you
can afford to take on the expenses for the person living in your own
home, you may find yourself financially strapped.

3–5. *Is a responsible adult available to watch the patient at home? Do
all adults in the family have to work outside the home? If yes, will there
be a responsible family member available to supervise care at home?*
Deciding on home care, without exploring the major issue of who will
be responsible for providing and/or supervising that care, is one of the
most unfortunate errors that families can commit. Not only should there
be a responsible adult available, but that adult should be knowledgeable,
capable, and understanding. If the person who assumes responsibility for

the home care has to work, even part-time, it is unfair to expect that individual to have the stamina needed to care for a frail person. Just because the family hires professional help, there is no reason to believe that it is not necessary for a family member to be around to supervise. And if there is a family member around to attend to the patient, a professional may still be required.

6. *Is there someone to relieve the primary family caregiver?* When the family will assume total responsibility for the care of the patient at home, that responsibility generally falls upon one person's shoulders—usually the daughter or daughter-in-law. This person has added a tremendous burden to her normal daily responsibilities, and that does not take into consideration her need for social activities. It is essential for this caregiver to be relieved from time to time, in order to reduce the frustration and anger that will ultimately affect the care of the patient.

7. *Are there young children at home who require supervision?* Young children demand a lot of attention from the family's primary caregiver. They have to be fed, dressed, and listened to. For schoolchildren, there is homework to be done, projects to be worked on, and activities to be supervised. There is a limited amount of time in the day, and time spent with the patient is time taken from the children.

8–9. *Are there teenage children at home? If there are, how will they feel about limiting their activities (friends dropping in, loud music, etc.)?* Grandchildren and grandparents often have special relationships, but teenage children have special needs, not the least of which is playing loud music, having friends in, coming in late, or talking endlessly on the phone. If the home is large enough to accommodate the often conflicting lifestyles of teenager and grandparent, these activities might not create a problem. However, the normal adolescent rebellion often requires exhaustive attention from parents.

10. *Do you have the emotional stability to deal with old people or sick people?* Disabilities in others strike a profound emotional reaction in ourselves. We can sympathize, empathize, or feel fear and strive for avoidance. The best health care professionals are those who can provide care in a nurturing, sensitive way, while maintaining a hint of detachment. This technique, not easily acquired, is often necessary for one's emotional health, when working with a very ill individual. It is almost impossible for family members to adopt that self-preserving attitude toward one of their own.

11. *Do you, yourself, fear the aging process?* Many people have biases against old and ailing individuals, not because of a lack of compassion, but because of identification, leading to fear. We are afraid of becoming old. We place a premium on the beauty of youth. If you do not look

young, you are ugly. We sometimes joke about having no option to growing older, yet that laughter masks a well-hidden concern. For some, this fear can be so consuming that having to live with an older person can result in emotional discomfort.

12–13. *Did you have a difficult time dealing with your mother or father? If yes, were these issues ever resolved?* The conflicts that were present between a parent and a child when they were both younger are now magnified by the age and infirmity of the parent and by the fact that the children too are growing older and possibly less tolerant. If the relationship was fraught with tension, if there were fights about curfew, children may find that, when an ill parent comes to live with them, the parent will still want to know where they are going and what time they will be home. Although adult children know they do not have to answer these questions, their emotional reaction may be based upon years of repressed frustration. It is easy, but also naïve, to think that children can dispassionately answer these questions now that they are adults. Emotions being what they are, and human nature being what it is, such is not the case. More often than not, children will find themselves reacting as they did when they were young.

14. *Is there a basic personality clash between you and your parent?* In the course of daily life, there are people we simply cannot get along with. Either they are too loud, too opinionated, too selfish, or too manipulative. We try to avoid these people. When we have to deal with them during working hours, we go about our business as rapidly as possible, glad we do not have to live with them. It is not unusual for these personality differences to occur between parent and child, and these differences must be considered before aging parent and adult child can live together.

15. *How would you feel providing care for your parent?* With this question, we begin to address the issue of role reversal. As parents age, their children often begin to assume certain responsibilities: they recommend doctors; help with finances; help with the shopping; and so forth. There are occasions when children have difficulty providing this type of care for their parents, accepting the parental role.

16. *How would you feel if you had to feed your parents or change their diapers?* Beyond the more "acceptable" types of care mentioned in the previous question, there are the highly private and more painful services to perform. We often overlook this aspect of home care, but these situations frequently occur and must be faced.

17–18. *Will the patient require a variety of rehabilitation programs, such as physical therapy, occupational therapy, speech therapy? If yes, are these programs available through home care services?* When the doctor tells you to "make arrangements," ask the doctor what kind of arrangements have to be made. Will the patient require physical therapy to relearn the use of a limb, or speech therapy to compensate for problems in communication? If these services are required, how will they be obtained? Will the patient have to be taken out of the home, or will the services be provided in the home? If the patient must be taken out for these services, who will be able to manage the transporting of the patient, particularly if therapy is required on a daily basis?

19–20. *Is home health care available in your community? If it is available, is there a long waiting list and limitations on the type or extent of care provided?* Even though a home care service may exist, it may not provide exactly what is needed. Some home care programs provide only housekeepers. If the patient needs medical treatment, the home care worker should be a registered or practical nurse. Begging the issue of type of care, what good will it do to have a home care service in the community that will enter the patient's name on a waiting list and perform an initial assessment, but not specify the starting date for care? The best advice: Do not be lax; explore what is needed before you need it.

21–22. *Has the patient always been a social individual? If yes, are there options for a variety of social activities at home?* No matter how ill or frail the patient, most people benefit from socialization. For the person who was always a social individual, this interaction is vital to a continued sense of well-being. Home care services generally do not provide social and recreational activities. In some neighborhoods, high school students volunteer to spend time with homebound elderly people. But most often, socialization is limited to a few brief conversations with the caregiver and a television set in the background. If that is the case, you can expect the patient to develop a sense of isolation and loneliness and possibly to become depressed.

If you have made any changes to your score, enter the revised total: _____. Once again, look at the assessment of your total score:

10 and under: You are a good candidate to provide home care.
11–20: Questionable.
21–30: Explore nursing homes. It may be the only answer, given honest responses to the quiz.

If, after taking this quiz, you find that nursing home care is a definite option, do not feel guilty about your choice. As we have seen in previous chapters, it will probably turn out to be the best decision for all involved. That is not to say that it will be easy for you, but you may find solace in the fact that you have made a decision based on many factors, not just emotion. If the reader is elderly and frail, their children will make the same reasonable decision to aid the reader. If you are opting for nursing home care, you can find additional help in pursuing this choice in the next chapter.

Chapter 8

Guidelines for Selecting a Nursing Home

There are approximately 20,000 nursing homes in the United States (Home Health Corporation of America, 1998). Of these, approximately 9,000 are skilled nursing facilities; the remainder are a combination of intermediate care, skilled nursing, and rehabilitation facilities. These 20,000 facilities fall into three categories: proprietary (privately owned); non-profit; and governmental (Harrington et al., 2002). Proprietary facilities are nursing homes designed as commercial profit-seeking ventures. There are about 15,000 private homes in the United States, clearly making up the majority. Nonprofit facilities (approximately 4,000) are generally religious or fraternal in nature. These homes are government-approved and therefore cannot discriminate against applicants, but religious and fraternal homes are inclined to accept individuals who are members of, or are referred by, the sponsoring order. Governmental homes, of which there are only about 1,000, are run under the direct sponsorship and supervision of the state in which they are located or of the federal government.

Understanding the types of facilities, what to look for, the decision-making process, and the emotional dynamics, is imperative. This chapter examines these issues and attempts to help families negotiate this process.

MAKING THE DECISION

The decision to place someone in a nursing home is not a simple one of merely making the decision and moving the patient in. There are many factors involved, which require contributions from several sources: the patient, the family, the doctor, the nursing home.

Often, families are forced to make a sudden decision. This can occur when a sudden illness requiring hospitalization and ongoing intensive care leaves little time and choice. The patient requires skilled nursing on a 24-hr basis, but cannot remain in the hospital, nor can the patient receive the necessary care at home. A bed is found in a nursing home, and things move very quickly.

In other situations, the decision to place an elderly family member in a nursing home is the result of a long-term attempt by the family to care for the elderly patient at home. In the latter case, the decision is usually resorted to when the patient's mental or physical deterioration makes it impossible for family members to continue caring for the elder at home.

Families are often left with many ambivalent feelings regarding the placement decision. However, all family members must recognize that, although their ill member may soon reside in a nursing home, they can remain involved in the caring process. Studies have consistently shown that family relationships that were strong before institutionalization remain so after, and those that were troubled or strained prior to the nursing home placement decision are likely to remain that way (Hook, Sobal, & Oak, 1982; Montgomery, 1982; Smith & Bengston, 1979).

THE DOCTOR

Usually, the elder's physician tells the family that there are no options other than a nursing home. The doctor's decision is based primarily on an awareness of the patient's physical and mental needs. This awareness is limited, but because the physician often does not know the family or their ability to provide home care, many physicians, particularly those specializing in geriatrics, take into account the amount of care the patient needs.

However, sometimes the doctor recommends that the patient follow through on the medical regimen prescribed, but says little more when the patient is discharged from the hospital. If this is the case, the family should ask the doctor for more specific information regarding the patient's functional abilities. It is not sufficient for the doctor to say, "Have him take his medicine, and I will see him in two weeks." If the patient is disabled by a stroke, for example, the family should know whether he will be able to dress and toilet himself, how much supervision he will need, and whether that supervision will require the services of a trained professional.

When a patient is discharged from a hospital, the physician usually works with a discharge planner (often a social worker) and the family.

This group has the responsibility of making a recommendation for follow-up care, and the discharge planner will usually make contact with the appropriate organizations. Sometimes, the discharge planner will even make arrangements for follow-up care at home or for a nursing home to send staff members to evaluate the patient for placement in their facility.

THE PATIENT

On occasion, a nursing home placement can be a sudden decision made by a family member in a time of crisis. The patient may be unable to participate in the decision-making process. There are situations, however, when the decision is made with forethought, involving a determined selection process, resulting in the best-conceived choice. The patient must recognize that the nursing home decision is based upon a consideration of the needs of all involved. This is best achieved in a family conference atmosphere, where the patient can at least hear the discussion. Even when the patient is unable to contribute, the decision should not be a dictatorial one.

Consideration should be given to the feelings of the older person, as well as of family members. Sharing these feelings openly and honestly will make it easier for the elderly individual to understand the placement decision as necessary, something that can be worked through (Silverman, Brahce, & Zielinski, 1981). There are nursing homes that will not allow families to dump their ailing elderly; they require that the patient be part of the decision-making process, for the benefit of the facility, as well as of the family. The best nursing homes provide an atmosphere in which the strengths of the residents are enhanced and their weaknesses minimalized.

FAMILY MEMBERS: DECIDING IN THE FACE OF GUILT

Steve R. has an elderly mother who is terminally ill, but who refuses to enter a nursing home. Steve and his sister, Sally, are sharing the responsibility of making sure that professional caregivers are in attendance. When the professionals are not available, Steve or Sally must be there. The caregivers sometimes come late, call in sick, or just do not show up. This happens a little too frequently. Sometimes, it is caused by weather or illness of the professional, but sometimes it is because the elderly woman can be very difficult. She always fires her assistants and asks them to do tasks that are not their responsibility.

The stress on Steve and Sally has been mounting. They both have jobs and need to work. They have used up all of their vacation time and almost all of their sick time. Steve could not make plans for a work-related trip that required an advance commitment of six months, because he did not know when his mother might need him. "This is no way for my mother and us to be," Steve commented, "but there is just no other choice." Someone suggested that the brother and sister consider a nursing home for their mother. "I could never do that to her. What, and dump her? Besides, when it was brought up, she had a fit."

Ginny's mother, Hilda, is 92 and legally blind. Ginny's brother, Joe, lives 800 miles away, so he is not available when Ginny needs help with Hilda's care. This happens from time to time, when the hired professionals do not show up, as in so many cases of this type. It has been Ginny's burden to return early from business trips or make calls wherever she is, in an attempt to get proper care for her mother. In general, she has put her mother's needs above her own life. Because Ginny was widowed in her early 40s and brought up four children alone, she expected these years to be *her* years, which unfortunately is not the case. When urged to put her mother in a nursing home, she replied, "She'll die there." When it was pointed out to her that indeed her mother might die there, because there was no expectation that she would return from the home, Ginny said it did not matter, she could never live with the guilt.

Most people view nursing homes as Steve and Ginny do—as places where old, sickly people are dumped, where they are brought to die. Just the thought of contacting these places causes family member to feel guilt. One often hears comments such as, "I'm not putting my mother in one of those awful places," "People die in nursing homes," "I can take care of my father all by myself," or "My husband will not survive without me." Many of these comments reflect legitimate views and beliefs. Some nursing homes may be awful, but not all of them are. Certainly, people die in nursing homes, but they also die in hospitals and at home, and families provide more care for their ill elderly members, with fewer resources, than ever before (Brody, 1985).

Often, those who decide that the nursing home is the correct option are faced with having to defend themselves against a barrage of "How can you do that to your mother?" Overall, the guilt that the family member endures defines the social stigma attached to the nursing home option. Guilt may be one of the few universal initial feelings associated with this stage of care. It is a legitimate feeling. As discussed in **Chapter 3,** the family members feel filial responsibility to their elderly members, a desire to pay back the bill of balanced responsibility and reciprocity, and a need to have immediate access to older generations.

Defining one's attitude about institutionalization is the first step in making the decision. Later in this chapter, we discuss how patients can be made to feel more comfortable with nursing home placement. In this section, we address the family members' attitudes.

Guilt occurs even when there is no other choice available. A positive attitude toward the possibility of nursing home placement, however, makes it easier to cope with this feeling. When the feelings regarding placement are ambivalent at best, learning to cope with the guilt is more difficult, but not impossible. It is sometimes helpful to reason things out in a clearly defined manner. Family members can make a list of the pros and cons of nursing home placement. All of the issues as the family perceives them should be entered. They will likely find that items on the pro side are all well reasoned; for example: "Nursing homes have round-the-clock care; I must work; the children need me." On the con side is a list of primarily emotional items: "I will feel like I am abandoning my mother; Dad will hate me for doing this to him; I feel as if I owe Mom so much more."

Guilt is an emotion, and it is charged by emotions. If family members can recognize the emotions and react to them on a more intellectual level, they will be better able to arrive at the most appropriate decision with the least anxiety. This is not to say that the feelings should be ignored. It does help, however, to view such feelings in the context of objective reality.

Another technique is to create a game plan. Families can make a list of all the people they know who were recently in the same predicament. Next, they check off those individuals with whom they can have an open and honest conversation. Their situations can be discussed. Why and how did they make their decisions? Families should not let the decision be made for them, but others' views should be listened to.

Finally, families can speak to a variety of professionals who have experience in this area. They can ask them to explain their views on the options. Which methods do they view as the best in your neighborhood, and why? Here too, decisions should not be made for the family members, but much information can be gained.

When an intelligent choice is made, families are less likely to be plagued by guilt. Most people have no clear understanding of nursing homes, because they never had to deal with them. They often find that their views are based on hearsay and bias. An individual having to choose between options must become as knowledgeable as possible.

WHAT TO LOOK FOR IN A NURSING HOME

One must look for the facility that provides the most appropriate care for the patient. It is conceivable that individuals with comparable ailments will thrive in different types of environments. Therefore, it is necessary not only to determine whether the nursing home can provide for the physical needs of the patient, but also whether the patient will do well emotionally in a particular setting.

A nursing home is not a hospital. For many people, the emphasis on nursing home care is on home. Matching the personality of the facility to that of the individual will result in a reciprocal adjustment. For instance, Bella A. was always interested in music. Even as her dementia worsened, she would still go over to the old piano in her sitting room and play Chopin. Bella's family, recognizing the importance of music in her life, looked for and found a facility that had a piano in every dayroom and that encouraged patients to use them.

Is there such a thing as a good nursing home? The answer is an unquestionable yes. Several lay publications have surveyed the field of nursing home care and have determined that there are many good facilities across the country. One of the most notable of these surveys, done several years ago, was published by *Good Housekeeping* (Abrams, 1985). The author indicated that there were at least 85 good nursing homes in the United States. This number is indeed quite low, in comparison to the total number of homes, but the survey included mostly nonprofit facilities, which are among the largest and best known. What made these facilities good are the things one should still look for. And these items can be found in many other smaller and less well-known homes.

As we have seen, making the decision is a difficult process, but once the decision to seek nursing home placement has been made, the research begins. This research requires several steps, including (1) seeking out the best facilities available, (2) visiting them several times, (3) meeting with the appropriate people at the facility, and (4) getting a feel for the facility, before a final decision is made. In order to find the best homes, individuals doing the research should know precisely what to look for. What follows is a basic guide to finding the home that is the best for all involved.

The first step in this research process is to develop a list of the most appropriate nursing homes. This list should be obtained through recommendations from health care professionals, the doctors involved in the case, the discharge planners at the hospital, local health care associations and senior citizen groups, the Web sites listed in **Chapter 9,** and others who have already been through this process (e.g. the American Nursing Home Association, n.d.). The list need not be long, but it should include several facilities with a good reputation. Further, as mentioned in chapter 2, the RUG reimbursement mechanism for nursing home care tends to favor certain illnesses, making it easier for patients with these illnesses to be admitted for nursing home care. Therefore, applications should be made to several appropriate sites.

There are three general categories of investigation: basics (licensure, costs, reputation); environmental issues; services.

Basics

Does the facility have a nursing home license? Not all facilities have government licenses; those that do are required to post the license publicly. If the license is not posted, or if the facility is unlicensed, it may mean that the facility is not maintaining a minimally acceptable level of care. In addition, third-party carriers (health care insurers) may not reimburse in the case of a facility that has no license.

Does the administrator have a nursing home administrator license? It is necessary that the administrator responsible for running the home be licensed, to ensure that the system runs according to basic standards. Some facilities have administrators who are not licensed, but are supervised by a consulting administrator who is.

Is the facility licensed by the Joint Commission on Accreditation of Health Care Organizations, the American Association of Homes for the Aging, or the American Nursing Home Association? Although these are not required affiliations, membership and approval by these organizations often indicate a greater willingness of the nursing home administration to comply voluntarily with professionally accepted standards.

What are the basic costs, and are all services included? Some facilities bill basic costs, then issue other bills for additional costs. Additional costs sometimes include linen, personal laundry, haircuts, dental care, and similar ancillary services. This is perfectly acceptable, as long as the family knows in advance what to expect.

What are the guidelines for the distribution of patients' spending money? Understanding what the facility's policy is and whether this policy will be acceptable to all involved is necessary, so that there will be no confusion in the future.

Does the facility encourage visitation both before and after placement? Many of the better facilities encourage prospective residents and their families to tour the facility and to ask questions, before a decision is made. If the facility is to be viewed as a home, a liberal visitation policy should exist once the family member becomes a resident.

How do staff members feel about the facility in which they work? Much of a nursing home's reputation is based on the morale of the staff.

Staff members should be willing to answer questions honestly and should be enthusiastic about their facility. In most cases, if nurses and ancillary staff are dissatisfied with the daily operation of the facility, there is an underlying reason. If the staff is unhappy, there is every likelihood that the patient will be unhappy as well.

Is the home following all basic requirements? Hallways should be well lighted; handrails and bars should be in place where they are necessary, especially in hallways and bathrooms; doors to stairways should be kept closed and should contain an alarm system; emergency evacuation plans should be posted throughout the facility.

Environmental Issues

Is the location a good one? The location should be pleasing to the patient, within easy traveling distance for family and friends.

Is the neighborhood safe for residents who are ambulatory? Nursing home patients are not necessarily restricted to the facility, and some consideration should be given to those who wish to go outside in nice weather. Is there a park-like area? Can patients walk the ground safely with some supervision? Are the grounds safe, attractive, and well maintained? Is there ample enclosed space for patients who are wanderers?

Does the nursing home have an agreement with a nearby hospital? An agreement between a nursing home and a local hospital is often necessary, to ensure that the patient is not sent out of the area if hospitalization is required. Some nursing homes are affiliated with teaching hospitals and maintain special training programs for geriatric doctors. These "teaching nursing homes," although on the forefront of geriatric care, do not necessarily guarantee a direct transfer agreement should hospitalization of a patient be required. The doctor attending the patient in the nursing home may have staff privileges at a different hospital; therefore, it is wise to determine in advance exactly where the patient will be placed, if it becomes necessary.

Is the appearance of the facility pleasing? A nursing home should be clean and well kept. It may be impossible to keep any health care facility totally odor-free and spotless, but it should be easy to determine if the housekeeping staff at the facility is doing a good job.

Do the patients look well cared for? Patients should be out of bed, clean, and dressed by midmorning. If this is not the case, there may be too few staff members to provide the needed care. The patients' physical appearance should indicate that they are being cared for. Their hair should be combed; clothing should be as clean and neat as possible.

Do patients and staff interact? Staff should interact with patients in a respectful fashion. The staff should be encouraging independence in the patients, while giving help when it is needed. Patients should feel comfortable with the staff members, and nurses, although often overwhelmed with the routine of necessary paperwork, should still find time to interact with patients.

What are the specific living arrangements? Will patients be required to share a room? Is there adequate space for personal possessions? Are the rooms well-heated and air-conditioned? Some facilities require that as many as four to six people share one large room. Other facilities have several private rooms. Closet space is understandably limited, but it should be adequate and accessible. The living environment should encourage a sense of comfort. All of the basic amenities should be clean and function appropriately. The home should be a comfortable place.

Services

What are the qualifications of the medical director? The better facilities have directors who have specialized in geriatrics, by training or experience. On the other hand, if this individual is on staff, but rarely at the facility, there is little benefit in having a name on a letterhead. The best medical directors are those who spend time at the home, know the patients, oversee the medical staff, know their limitations, and ask for the help of other specialists when necessary.

Are private physicians allowed? Many facilities allow only a small panel of doctors to act as attending physicians to the residents. If this is the case, it is not inappropriate to ask to interview the doctor who will be assigned to attend the patient. If you are unhappy with that physician, ask to be assigned to another.

What are the provisions for dental care, podiatry, eye care, and mental health? A staff of consulting specialists should be under contract to provide these services. One should ask to see the list of providers and inquire how available they are to the patients and how often they attend the facility.

Is the nursing staff supervised by a registered professional? The director of nursing should be a registered nurse with experience in clinical and administrative care of the elderly.

Is the nursing staff adequate for the number of patients? Different levels of care require different patient-to-staff ratios, but staff should not appear regularly overworked and harried.

Are rehabilitation services available at the facility? The nursing home should have a staff that provides physical, occupational, and speech therapy at the facility. Checking to see the room in which these services are provided, and the ways the therapy is carried out, will give some insight into how dedicated the facility is to this important component of care.

Is there a qualified social worker on staff? Many facilities employ social service assistants to work under the direction of a certified social worker. This supervisor should be at the facility regularly. Social work staff should be dedicated, performing more than basic paper-compliance work, interacting regularly with the patients.

Is there a recreation staff with an appropriate program? Most facilities have recreation and socialization staff. It is important to determine, however, whether the programs are actually carried out and whether the activities are correct for the patients. The recreation leaders should not be infantalizing, nor should they conduct programs that are beyond the residents' intellectual or cognitive skills.

Are religious needs attended to? The facility should have a chapel, and members of the clergy should attend the facility to provide regular services, offer counseling, act as friendly visitors, and even conduct classes. Clergy of all religions should be available at the nursing home.

Is the dietary department well equipped? When reviewing a nursing home, one should take the time to see how the food is distributed at mealtime. Is it presented in an appetizing fashion? Are the foods hot that are meant to be hot? Ask how special diets are handled, and visit the facility's kitchen. It should be clean and run efficiently.

These questions represent basic guidelines, but they are not exhaustive. Individuals exploring nursing home care should ask more questions. They should visit the facilities they think best several times and at different times of the day. Although the decision is not an easy one, knowing that you have selected the best possible nursing home can be emotionally soothing.

PAYING FOR CARE

When the process of selecting the best facility has begun, one must also begin to answer the question of how to pay for the care. The cost for providing long-term care can range from $9,000 to $90,000 per year, or even more. Not much has changed since a *New York Times* article (Kazdin, 1988), in which a daughter bemoans the fact that the only advice her mother has received to help pay for her father's nursing home care is to divorce her husband. By doing so, the mother can maintain some of her assets while the father "spends down" his assets and becomes eligible for Medicaid.

Medicaid

Medicaid is a federal and state program designed to provide health care insurance to low-income individuals; 50% to 85% of the program is funded by the federal government, the remainder by the states. States contribute different amounts. Guidelines for eligibility in the program vary from state to state, depending on the state's residency and income requirements. Some states admit individuals whose total assets are above the minimal poverty level to the program if their medical expenses are excessively high.

Medicaid pays for nursing home care, if the facility is certified by the program. Payments are made directly from the state Medicaid office to the health care provider for home or nursing home care. Because eligibility for the Medicaid program is determined solely by financial need, the department that determines an individual's need will request information regarding all assets, including residence, income, real and personal property, medical expenses, and family composition. If total assets exceed the requirements for eligibility, payment may have to come from one's pocket and will continue until total assets have dwindled to the level at which the patient becomes eligible for Medicaid. This is referred to as "spenddown."

A stigma is still attached to applying for Medicaid, although this should not be the case. The program is totally funded by taxes to which most citizens have contributed. Perhaps the stigma is because one must be impoverished to be eligible. After working all of one's life, not having the means to pay for one's care can be very demoralizing.

Medicare

Medicaid is available for any eligible person, regardless of age, but Medicare is a federally funded health insurance program for individuals over the age of 65. There are no financial requirements or restrictions; everyone 65 or older who qualifies for Social Security is eligible for Medicare.

Under the Catastrophic Health Insurance bill, which took effect January 1, 1989, Medicare expanded its coverage and increased the services covered, helping to ward off the financial ruin that often accompanies catastrophic illness.

Medicare has two parts. Part A is the hospital insurance portion; Part B, the physician/medical insurance portion. The legislation provides for Part A to cover unlimited hospital care, after a deductible is met. Part B has a yearly out-of-pocket expenses limit, after which Medicare takes care of all expenses. An interesting addition in the law is the coverage of outpatient prescription drugs. Beginning in 1991, 50% of the cost of prescription drugs were paid, after the individual paid the first $600; in 1992, the percentage covered rose to 60%; in 1993, it rose to 80%. In addition, the law provided that Medicare will cover the cost of 7 days per week of home health care, to a limit of 38 days per illness. The skilled nursing care benefit also increased, from 100 to 150 days. Although there have been attempts to increase drug benefits under Medicare, that has not yet occurred. For current information, check the Center for Medicare and Medicaid Services Web page at www.medicare.gov.

The home health care services covered by Medicare include part-time skilled nursing care, physical therapy, speech therapy, and part-time services of a home health aide. Some medical supplies and 80% of costs of durable medical equipment are also covered. Medicare will not cover full-time nursing care at home, medications, meals, and homemaker services.

In order to cover the costs of this policy, a surtax or "supplemental premium" began to be charged. Initially, the supplemental premium amounted to $48 per year, but increased to 28% of taxable income in 1993 (with a ceiling of $1,050). The $48 premium applied to single individuals with a maximum yearly income of $10,000. The total maximum premium is approximately $2,000, and that applies to married couples earning more than $90,000 annually.

The legislation also affected Medicaid in one critical area: State Medicaid programs must allow the spouses of residents of skilled nursing facilities to keep a specified amount of their monthly income and up to half the couple's total assets, with states having the option of allowing individuals to shelter assets to a current maximum of $60,000. For current information, the Center for Medicare and Medicaid Services' Web site should always be consulted (www.medicare.gov).

The legislation was designed to enhance the programs that provide care and also to enhance coverage to an estimated 30 million Medicare beneficiaries, by eliminating some of the financial hardship, but critics have suggested that the law still omits many long-term care services (Butler, 1988). In particular, the law does not provide coverage for victims of Alzheimer's disease, and the coverage for nursing home and home care is considered sparse.

In addition to these shortcomings in the Medicare Catastrophic Protection Act, the funding for the program is collected from a premium assessed on individuals eligible for Medicare. The assessment is based on federal income tax liability. Thus, an individual with a high income from tax-free investments might be assessed at a lower rate than someone with a lower income from taxable sources. All these figures are subject to change. To stay on top of these changes, consult the Medicare Web page at www.medicare.gov.

Private Insurance

More than 200,000 older Americans are estimated to be presently covered by approximately 60 private long-term care insurers (Lane, 1986). Many of these policies provide a daily outlay of cash to the policyholder, rather than reimbursing for medical bills (Champlin, 1988). These policies cover home health services (in some instances) and nursing home care (Health Insurance Association of America, 1988). Critics have found that many of the policies are too expensive for most elderly individuals and that, in some cases, the benefits do not make up for the high costs.

A review several years ago found that many long-term care policies will never pay benefits to subscribers ("What's New," 1988). The study reviewed 77 plans offered by 21 companies. In general, the restrictions, including requiring previous hospitalization or skilled nursing prior to nursing home entry, make the probability of collecting from these plans only about 39%.

Long-Term Care Insurance

Since that study was performed in 1988, there have been many changes in private insurance, with the estimated average cost for long-term care currently hovering around $55,000 to $60,000. This is expected to grow as much as 30%. A greater than 50% chance exists that some form of long-term care will be needed after age 65, and the need for long-term care insurance that is effective continues to grow (General Accounting Office, 2000). When investigating long-term care insurance, there are five important variables to explore:

1. The maximum daily benefit, or amount the policy will pay;
2. The total benefit, or maximum amount the policy will provide for long-term care;
3. The waiting period, sometimes referred to as the elimination period, which is the amount of time you must wait prior to the benefits starting;
4. Protection from inflation, to keep up with the rising costs of long-term care; and
5. Facilities covered, including care at home and assisted living centers (or is it limited only to skilled nursing facilities?).

PREPARING THE PATIENT TO ACCEPT
A NURSING HOME

Once the decisions have been made, it is time to deal with the transition to nursing home life. There are useful techniques to deal with stressful reactions that may occur.

It is not helpful when family members talk of the placement decision in whispers and do not include the patient as part of the decision-making process. Hiding emotions and concerns is not only detrimental, but hinders the adjustment process.

The psychological and physical needs of the patient must be taken into consideration. For a resident to become comfortable in a new setting, there has to be an interface between the needs of the patient and the workings of the facility. In order for this meshing to be most successful, the prospective resident must be informed about the new home. Whenever possible, the patient should have the responsibility of deciding which is the best facility. This may be an inconvenience to some family members, but the sense of control that it affords the older person is essential. Similarly, whenever possible, the older person should be involved in deciding the status of personal belongings—which should be saved, which sold or given away, which taken to the new location. The more involved the patient, the less the feeling of having no voice in the matter. Individuals who feel that they have been forced into decisions will almost always rebel against the change.

Part of the admission process includes dealing with subjects that may be sensitive, awkward, or even embarrassing. Ignoring these topics does not make them go away. Discussing them, despite the initial discomfort, contributes to a sense of familiarity and allows the individual to better comprehend the change about to take place. It is important to talk about other residents at the facility, roommates, food, staff, activities, visiting schedules, and privacy. The prospective resident has the right to know who a roommate will be and what will happen if they cannot get along. The individual must also be apprised of the recreational and socialization activities, so that those most appropriate can be joined as soon as possible. The patient must also know who the direct care providers will be (the doctor, nurses, aides, and therapists) and the medical routines that they will be expected to follow.

Many family members dismiss the idea of discussion with the statement, "She's too confused to understand." This sentiment is rarely true. Even when the patient's cognitive skills are compromised, there is usually sufficient awareness that a change is occurring. To deny this fact is to ignore the patient for the sake of expediency. Involving the patients, to the degree that they can be involved, inevitably makes the transition to the nursing home less traumatic.

The transition may become difficult in spite of the best efforts of the family and professionals. The patient may not accept placement or may become disenchanted with placement shortly after arriving at the facility. The period of adjustment to a new setting can last as long as 7 or 8 months. During that time, physical and emotional deterioration may occur. This does not necessarily mean that the patient will not adjust. The worst thing that a family member can do is overreact to these changes; frequently, they are transitory, and nursing home professionals have a great deal of experience in dealing with this problem. Although a family member may have difficulty seeing a loved one in this condition, becoming agitated only heightens the difficulty the resident is experiencing.

Complaining and criticizing are appropriate behaviors for an elderly person going through a drastic change. Similarly, family members have the right to criticize and complain; however, the complaints should be to the right person in a private, uncritical fashion, offered as an observation or suggestion (York, 1984).

If the complaints of the loved one appear unjustified, they should not be rejected out-of-hand. Instead, it is important to listen to the feelings that cause the individual to complain. The actual complaint may be erroneous, but the underlying emotion may be legitimate. Sometimes, just listening, allowing the individual the opportunity to vent, is sufficient. This shows the patient that she has not been rejected and that the family remains available to provide support. However, it is sometimes necessary to point out, gently but firmly, that the patient is being unreasonable and not giving the placement a fair chance.

Adjusting to a nursing home means different things to different people. Some patients may enter into a state of passive acceptance. They do what is expected of them and follow the routines, but are not involved. Other individuals seem to be actively involved in all of the facility's programs. Adjustment has more to do with long-term personality characteristics than with the nursing home environment per se. Some people are lifelong active participants, and others are lifelong active observers (Salamon, 1988).

As seen in previous chapters, most residents of nursing homes are satisfied with their lives; satisfaction includes adjustment. Given the proper support in the right setting, the transition to a nursing home can be accomplished with a minimum of stress for all parties.

Chapter 9

Nursing Home Resources and Associations

There are many organizations ready and eager to provide answers to all questions about selecting a nursing home or to review other options. These important decisions can be made with knowledge and confidence, and without guilt, once all the factors necessary for appropriate action are taken into consideration.

The following national organizations have materials that can provide useful information about nursing homes and other long-term care institutions serving the elderly. They are all useful sources, but each has a different focus, as noted:

American Association of Homes and Services for the Aging
2519 Connecticut Avenue NW
Washington, DC 20008-1520
Phone:(202)783-2242
Fax: (202)783-2254
Web: adc@aahsa.org

American College of Health Care Administrators (ACHCA)
300 N. Lee Street, Suite 301
Alexandria, VA 22314
Phone: (703)739-7900
(888)88-ACHCA
Fax: (703)739-7901
www.ACHCA.org

Board of Nursing Home Administrators
239 Causeway Street, Suite 500
Boston, MA 02114
Phone: (617)727-9925

American Health Care Association (AHCA)
1201 L Street NW
Washington, DC 20005
Phone: (202)842-4444
(202)842-3860
www.ahca.org

National Center for Assisted Living
Phone: (202)842-4444
www.ncal.org

National Council on the Aging
409 Third Street SW, Suite 200
Washington, DC 20024
Phone: (202)479-1200
Fax: (202)479-0735
www.ncoa.org

Alzheimer's Disease and Related Disorders
www.alzweb.org

National Association of Home Care
www.NAHC.org

Select Home Health Agencies of America
www.carescout.com

National Citizens' Coalition for Nursing Home Reform
1424 16th Street NW, Suite 202
Washington, DC 20036
Phone: (202)332-2276
Fax: (202)332-2949
www.nccnhr.org

American Association of Retired Persons
601 E Street NW
Washington, DC 20049

Phone: (800)424-3410
www.aarp.org

American Foundation for the Blind
11 Penn Plaza, Suite 300
New York, NY 10001
Phone: (800)232-5463
www.afbinfo@afb.net; www.afb.org

Often, adults who live at a distance from their elderly parents find that their parents are becoming increasingly frail and require a variety of services. It is not always easy for the children to travel great distances to check up on the parents. To deal with this issue of obtaining long-distance care for elderly relatives who live far away, several organizations have evolved. These organizations provide on-site care managers and act as surrogates for the family. They attempt to arrange the necessary services, and they report to the family.

There is presently no supervisory organization or council that oversees care management groups, but that is likely to develop over the next few years. The following are reference and service groups.

Center for Medicare & Medicaid Services (CMS)
(formerly Health Care Financing Administration)
7500 Security Blvd.
Baltimore, MD 21244
Phone (410)786-3000
www.medicare.gov

Also see:
www.medicare.gov/NHCompare/home.asp

The following Web sites rank the variety of services available for the provision of care:

www.eldercare.gov—Eldercare locater.

www.memberofthefamily.net—This site contains an honor roll of the best programs, a national watchlist, and how to contact ombudsmen.

www.premiercareguide.com—Explains methodology for ranking programs using several different sets of available data, and provides written reports on specific facilities for reasonable fees.

www.healthgrades.com—In conjunction with J.D. Power & Associates, provides ratings and profiles for hospitals, physicians, nursing homes, and home care agencies.

www.carescout.com—Nursing home, assisted living, home health, and hospital ratings; reports available for a fee.

Children of Aging Parents
1609 Woodbourne Road
Levittown, PA 19057
Phone: (800)227-7294
www.caps4caregivers.org

For information regarding insurance and health benefits, see the following Web sites:

Long-term care insurance
www.insure.com/ltc

National Council on the Aging's Benefits Check-Up
www.benefitscheckup.org

Each state and territory in the United States has an organization designed to act as an advocate for older adults. These state and regional offices on aging provide information about programs and services. They also act as coordinators of activities and are an excellent source of referral information. The following is a directory of state agencies and regional offices. One may access local agencies on aging through:

Administration on Aging
Phone: (800)677-1116
www.aoa.gov

Alabama
Commission on Aging
770 Washington Ave.
RSA Plaza, Suite 470
Montgomery, AL 36130
Phone: (334)242-5743

Alaska
Older Alaskans Commission

3601 C Street, Suite 260
Anchorage, AK 99503-5209
Phone: (907)563-6393
Hotline: (800)478-9996

Arizona
Aging and Adult Administration
1789 West Jefferson, Suite 950A
Phoenix, AZ 85007
Phone: (602)542-4446

Arkansas
Division of Aging and Adult Services
P.O. Box 1437, Slot 1412
Little Rock, AR 72201-1437
Phone: (501)682-2441

California
Department of Aging
1600 K Street
Sacramento, CA 95814
Phone: (916)323-6681

Colorado
The Legal Center
455 Sherman Street, Suite 130
Denver, CO 80203
Phone: (303)722-0300

Connecticut
Department of Aging
Elderly Services Division
3580 Main Street
Hartford, CT 06106
Phone: (860)723-1390

Delaware
Services for Aging and Disabled
 Health and Social Services
Oxford Building
256 Chapman Road, Suite 200
Newark, DE 19702
Phone: (302)577-4791

District of Columbia
AARP, Legal Counsel for the Elderly
601 E. Street NW, 4th Floor, Bldg. A
Washington, DC 20049
Phone: (202)434-2140

Florida
State LTC Ombudsman
600 South Calhoun Street, Suite 270
Tallahassee, FL 32301
Phone: (850)488-6190

Georgia
Division of Aging Services
2 Peachtree Street NW, Suite 36-233
Atlanta, GA 30303-3142
Phone: (888)454-5826

Hawaii
Office of the Governor
Executive Office on Aging
250 South Hotel Street, Suite 107
Honolulu, HI 96813-2831
Phone: (808)586-0100

Idaho
Commission on Aging
P.O. Box 83720
Boise, IA 83720-0007
Phone: (208)334-3833

Illinois
Department on Aging
421 East Capitol Avenue, Suite 100
Springfield, IL 62701-1789
Phone: (800)252-8966
(217)785-3143

Indiana
Division of Aging and Rehabilitation Services
402 W. Washington Street, Suite W-454
Indianapolis, IN 46204
Phone: (317)232-7134

Iowa
Department of Elder Affairs
914 Grand Avenue, No. 236
Jewett Bldg.
Des Moines, IA 50319
Phone: (515)281-8643

Kansas
LTC Ombudsman
610 S.W. 10th Street, 2nd Floor
Topeka, KS 66612-1616
Phone: (785)296-3017

Kentucky
Division of Aging Services
275 E. Main Street, 5th Floor
Frankfort, KY 40621
Phone: (502)564-6930

Louisiana
Governor's Office of Elderly Affairs
412 N. 4th Street, 3rd Floor
P.O. Box 80374
Baton Rouge, LA 70802
Phone: (225)342-7100

Maine
Ombudsmen
1 Weston Court
P.O. Box 128
Augusta, ME 04332
Phone: (207)621-1079

Maryland
Office of Aging
301 W. Preston Street, Room 1007
Baltimore, MD 21201
Phone: (410)767-1074

Massachusetts
Executive Office of Elder Affairs
1 Ashburton Place, 5th Floor

Boston, MA 02108-1518
Phone: (617)727-7750

Michigan
Citizens for Better Care
4750 Woodward Avenue, Suite 410
Detroit, MI 48201-3908
Phone: (313)832-6387

Minnesota
Office of Ombudsman
121 East Seventh Place, Suite 410
St. Paul, MN 55101
Phone: (651)296-0382

Mississippi
Division of Aging and Adult Services
750 N. State Street
Jackson, MS 39202
Phone: (601)359-4929

Missouri
Division of Aging
Department of Social Services
P.O. Box 1337
Jefferson City, MO 65102-1337
Phone: (573)526-0727

Montana
Office on Aging
Department of Health and Human Services
P.O. Box 4210
Helena, MT 59604-4210
Phone: (406)444-4077

Nebraska
Department on Aging
301 Centennial Mall South
P.O. Box 95044
Lincoln, NE 68509-5044
Phone: (402)471-2306

Nevada
Division for Aging Services
Department of Human Resources
340 N. 11th Street, Suite 203
Las Vegas, NV 89101
Phone: (702)486-3545

New Hampshire
Division of Elderly and Adult Services
129 Pleasant Street
Concord, NH 03301-3857
Phone: (603)271-4375

New Jersey
Ombudsman
P.O. Box 807
Trenton, NJ 08625-0807
Phone: (609)588-3614

New Mexico
Agency on Aging
228 E. Palace Avenue
Santa Fe, NM 87501
Phone: (505)827-7640

New York
Office of Aging
Agency Bldg. 2
2 Empire State Plaza
Albany, NY 12223-0001
Phone: (518)474-7329

North Carolina
Division of Aging
693 Palmer Drive
Raleigh, NC 27626-0531
Phone: (919)733-8395

North Dakota
Department of Human Services
Aging Service Division
600 South 2nd Street, Suite 1C
Bismark, ND 58504
Phone: (701)328-8910

Ohio
Department of Aging
50 W. Broad Street, 9th Floor
Columbus, OH 43215-5928
Phone: (614)466-1221

Oklahoma
Department of Human Services
Aging Services Division
312 NE 28th Street, Suite 109
Oklahoma City, OK 73105
Phone: (405)521-6734

Oregon
Ombudsman
3855 Wolverine NE, Suite 6
Salem, OR 97305-1251
Phone: (503)378-6533

Pennsylvania
Department of Aging
555 Walnut Street, 5th Floor
P.O. Box 1089
Harrisburg, PA 17101
Phone: (717)783-7247

Puerto Rico
Ombudsman
Call Box 50063
Old San Juan Station
San Juan, Puerto Rico 00902
Phone: (787)725-1515

Rhode Island
Ombudsman
422 Post Road, Suite 204
Warwick, RI 02888
Phone: (401)785-3340

South Carolina
Division on Aging
1801 Main Street

P.O. Box 8206
Columbia, SC 29202-8206
Phone: (803)898-2580

South Dakota
Office of Adult Services and Aging
Ombudsman
700 Governors Drive
Pierre, SD 57501-2291
Phone: (605)773-3656

Tennessee
State LTC Ombudsman
Commission on Aging
Andrew Jackson Building
500 Deaderick Street, 9th Floor
Nashville, TN 37243-0860
State has Regional Ombudsman.
For referral, call: (615)741-2056

Texas
Department on Aging
P.O. Box 12786
Austin, TX 78751-2316
Phone: (512)424-6840

Utah
Department of Social Services
Division of Aging and Adult Services
120 North 200 West, Room 401
Salt Lake City, UT 84103
Phone: (801)538-3924

Vermont
Ombudsman, Legal Aid
264 N. Winooski
Burlington, VT 05402
Phone: (802)863-5620

Virginia
Association of Area Agencies on Aging
530 East Main Street, Suite 428
Richmond, VA 23219
Phone: (804)644-2923

Washington
S. King County Multi-Service Center
P.O. Box 23699
Federal Way, WA 98093
Phone: (253)838-6810

West Virginia
Commission on Aging
1900 Kanawha Blvd. East
Charleston, WV 25305-0160
Phone: (304)558-3317

Wisconsin
Board on Aging and Long-Term Care
214 North Hamilton Street
Madison, WI 53703-2118
Phone: (608)266-8945 Ext. DIR

Wyoming
Senior Citizen, Inc.
756 Gilchrist, P.O. Box 94
Wheatland, WY 82201
Phone: (307)322-5553

References

Abrams, M. (1985, August). 85 best nursing homes. *Good Housekeeping*, 67–70.

Adams, D. L. (1969). Analysis of a life satisfaction index. *Journal of Gerontology, 24,* 470–474.

Administration on Aging. (2001). *The older population: A profile of older Americans, 2001.* Washington, DC.

Alexopoulos, G. S. (1996). Geriatric depression in primary care. *International Journal of Geriatric Psychiatry, 11,* 397–400.

American Health Care Association. (1984). *Facts in brief on long-term health care.* Washington, DC. Author.

American Health Care Association. (1999). *Facts and trends, 1999: The nursing facility sourcebook,* Washington, DC: AHCA.

American Nursing Home Association. (n.d.). *Thinking about a nursing home.* Washington, DC: NHA. Pub. 0773-2.

Aquino, J. A., Russel, D. W., Cutrona, C. E., & Altmaier, E. M. (1996). Employment status, social support and life satisfaction among the elderly. *Journal of Counseling Psychology, 43,* 480–489.

Assisted Living Quality Coalition (1998). *Assisted living quality initiative: Building a structure that promotes quality.* Washington, DC. Author.

Association of American Medical Colleges. (1999). *Curriculum directory.* Washington, DC: AAMC.

Barry, J. R. (1980). Counseling the aging. *Personnel and Guidance Journal, 59,* 122–124.

Beland, F. (1986). The clientele of comprehensive and traditional home care programs. *The Gerontologist, 26,* 382–388.

Bishop, C. E., Kerwin, J., & Wallack, S. S. (1999). The Medicare home health benefit implications of recent payment changes. *Care Management Journals, 1,* 189–196.

Blazer, D. (1990). *Emotional problems in later life: Intervention strategies for professional caregivers.* New York: Springer Publishing.

Bookwala, J., & Schulz, R. (1996). Spousal similarity in subjective well-being. *Psychology and Aging, 11,* 582–590.

Borup, J. H. (1982). The effects of varying degrees of interinstitutional environmental change on long-term care patients. *The Gerontologist, 22,* 409–417.

Bradburn, N., & Caplovits, D. (1965). *Reports on happiness.* Chicago: Aldine Press.

Brody, E. M. (1984). Women in the middle. *The Gerontologist, 21,* 471–480.

Brody, E. M. (1985, July 9). Health care cost-containment: Are America's aged protected? Testimony before the House Select Committee on Aging, 2.

Brody, E. M., Johnsen, P. T., Fulcomer, M. C., & Lang, A. M. (1983). Women's changing roles and help to the elderly: Attitudes of three generations of women. *Journal of Gerontology, 38,* 597–607.

Butler, R. N. (1975). *Why survive? Being old in America.* New York: Harper & Row.

Butler, R. (1988). Catastrophic coverage: Good, but we can do better. *Geriatrics, 43,* 110–114.

Butler, R. N., Grossman, L. K., & Oberlink, M. R. (Eds.) (1999). *Life in an older America.* New York: Century Foundation Press.

Campbell, A., Converse, P. E., & Rogers, W. L. (1976). *Quality of American life.* New York: Russel Sage Foundation.

Cantor, M. H. (1983). Strain among caregivers: A study of experiences in the United States. *The Gerontologist, 23,* 601–610.

Capitman, J. A. (1986). Community-based long-term care models: Target groups and impacts on service use. *The Gerontologist, 26,* 389–397.

Carp, F. M. (1977). Morale: What questions are we asking of whom? In C. N. Nydeggar (Ed.), *Measuring morale: A guide to effective assessment.* Washington, DC: Gerontological Society of America.

Castle, N. G. (2001). Innovation in nursing homes: Which facilities are the early adopters? *The Gerontologist, 41,* 161–172.

Cavan, R. S., Burges, E. W., Havighurst, R. J., & Goldhammer, H. (1949). *Personal adjustment in old age.* Chicago: Science Research Associates.

Champlin, L. (1988). Long-term care: Protecting the elderly from going broke. *Geriatrics, 43,* 96–102.

Chappell, S. (1994). Home care research. What does it tell us? *The Gerontologist, 34,* 116–120.

Chenoweth, B., & Spencer, B. (1986). Dementia: The experience of family caregivers. *The Gerontologist, 26,* 267–272.

Citro, J., & Hermanson, S. (1999). Assisted living in the United States. AARP Working Paper. Washington, DC: American Association of Retired Persons, Public Policy Institute.

Conner, K. A., Powers, E. A., & Bultena, G. L. (1979). Social interactions and life satisfaction: An empirical assessment of late life patterns. *Journal of Gerontology, 34,* 116–121.

Conte, V. A., & Salamon, M. J. (1982). An objective approach to the measurement and use of life satisfaction. *Measurement and Evaluation in Guidance, 15,* 194–200.

Costa, P. T., & McCrae, R. R. (1980). Still stable after all these years: Personality as a key to some issues in adulthood and old age. In P. B. Baltes & O. G. Brim (Eds.), *Life span development and behavior* (Vol. 3). New York: Academic Press.

Covey, H. C. (1981). A reconceptualization of continuity theory: Some preliminary thoughts. *The Gerontologist, 12,* 628–633.

Csikszentmihalyi, M. (1999) If we are so rich, why aren't we happy? *American Psychologist, 54,* 821–827.

Cumming, E. M., & Henry, W. (1961). *Growing old.* New York: Basic Books.

Cutillo-Schmitter, T. A., Zisselman, M., & Woldow, A. (1999). Life satisfaction in centerians residing in long-term care. *Annals of Long-Term Care, 7,* 437–442.

Cutler, N. E. (1979). Age variations in the dimensionality of life satisfaction. *Journal of Gerontology, 34,* 573–578.

Cutler, S. J. (1973). Voluntary association participation and life satisfaction. A cautionary research note. *Journal of Gerontology, 28,* 497–502.

Danger, J. (2002). Nursing home statistics. Retrieved August 6, 2002, from http://jeffdanger.com/statistics.htm

Diener, E. (2000). Subjective well-being: The science of happiness and a proposal for a national index. *American Psychologist, 55,* 34–43.

Edwards, J., & Klemmack, L. (1973). Correlates of life satisfaction: A re-examination. *Journal of Gerontology, 28,* 497–502.

Erickson, M. A., Dempster-McCain, D., Whitlow, C., & Moen, P. (2000). Does moving to a continuing care retirement community reduce or enhance social integration. Retrieved October 31, 2002, from http://www.pathwayslifequality.org/wp00_09.html

Finlayson, M. (2002). Changes predicting long-term use among the oldest-old. *The Gerontologist, 32,* 665–672.

Fransella, F., & Dalton, P. (1990). *Personal construct counseling in action.* Newbury, CA: Sage.

French, H. W. (1988, August 24). Nursing home payments faulted as too selective. *The New York Times,* B1–B5.

Fry, P. S. (2000). Religious involvement, spirituality, and personal meaning for life: Existential predictors of psychological well-being in community-residing and institutional care elders. *Aging and Mental Health: An International Journal, 4,* 375–387.

General Accounting Office. (2000). *Long-term care insurance: Better information critical to prospective purchasers.* T-HES-00-196. Available on www.GAO.gov

George, L. K. (1979). The happiness syndrome: Methodological and substantive issues in the study of social-psychological well-being in adulthood. *The Gerontologist, 26,* 253–259.

George, L. K. (1984). The institutionalized. In E. B. Palmore (Ed.), *Handbook on the aged in the United States.* Westport, CT: Greenwood Press.

George, L. K., & Landerman, R. (1984). Health and subjective well-being. A replicated secondary data analysis. *International Journal of Aging and Human Development, 19,* 133–155.

Gilford, R. (1984). Contrasts in marital satisfaction throughout old age. An exchange theory analysis. *Journal of Gerontology, 39,* 325–333.

Gilson, R., Waldo, D., & Levit, K. (1983). National health expenditures, 1982. *Health Care Financing Review, 5,* 1–32.

Gray, G. R., Ventis, D. G., & Hayslip, B. (1972). Sociocognitive skills as a determinant of life satisfaction in aged persons. *International Journal of Aging and Human Development, 35,* 205–218.

Haley, W. E., Levine, E. G., Brown, S. L., & Bartolucci, A. A. (1987). Stress appraisal, coping and social support as predictors of adaptational outcome among dementia caregivers. *Psychology and Aging, 2,* 323–330.

Harrington, C., Carillo, H., Thollaug, S., Summers, P., & Wellin, V. (2002) Nursing facilities staffing, residents, and facility deficiencies, 1993–1999. Retrieved October 23, 2002, from http://www.hcfa. gov/Medicaid/ltchomep

Harrington, C., Swan, J. H., Bedney, B., Carillo, H., & Struder, L. (1996). *1995 State data book on long-term care: Program and market characteristics.* San Francisco: University of California.

Haug, M. R. (1985). Home care for the ill elderly: Who benefits? *American Journal of Public Health, 75,* 127–128.

Hawes, C., & Phillips, C. D. (2000). High service or high privacy assisted living facilities, their residents and staff: Results from a national survey, November 2000. U.S. Department of Health and Human Services. Retrieved October 15, 2002 from http://www. aspe.hhs. gov/daltcp/reports/hshp.htm

Health Insurance Association of America. (1988). *The Consumer's Guide to Long-Term Care Insurance.* Washington, DC: HIAA.

Heffler, S., Levit, K., Smith, S., Smith, C., Cowan, C., & Lazenby, H. (2001). Health spending growth up in 1999: Faster growth expected in the future. *Health Affairs, 20,* 193–203.

Hendrick, S. S., & Hendrick, C. (1997). Love and satisfaction. In R. J. Sternberg & M. Hojjat (Eds.), *Satisfaction in close relationships.* New York: Guilford Press.

Holahan, C. K. (1981). Lifetime achievement patterns, retirement and life satisfaction of gifted aged women. *Journal of Gerontology, 36,* 741–749.

Hook, W. F., Sobal, J., & Oak, J. C. (1982). Frequency of visitation in nursing home: Patterns of contact across barriers in total institutions. *The Gerontologist, 22,* 324–428.

Hooker, K., Manoogian-O'Dell, M., Monahan, D. J., Frazier, L. D., & Shifren, K. (2000). Does type of disease matter? Gender differences among Alzheimer's and Parkinson's disease spouse caregivers. *The Gerontologist, 40,* 568–573.

Horowitz, A., & Shindelman, L. W. (1983). Reciprocity and affection: Past influences on current caregiving. *Journal of Gerontology, 16,* 67–70.

Howell, N. M., Proctor, E., & Rosario, P. (2001). How much is enough? Perspectives of care recipients and professionals of the sufficiency of home care. *The Gerontologist, 41,* 723–732.

Kahana, E. (1975). Matching environments to the needs of the aged: A conceptual scheme. In J. Gibrium (Ed.), *Psychosocial care of the dying.* New York: McGraw–Hill.

Kahana, E., & Kahana, B. (1985). Institutionalization—bane or blessing. In A. M. Haug, A. B. Ford, & M. Scheafor (Eds.), *The mental and physical health of aged women.* New York: Springer Publishing.

Kane, R. A., & Kane, R. L. (1981). *Assessing the elderly: A practical guide to measurement.* Lexington, MA: Lexington Books.

Kaplan, B., Campbell, J. C., & Gore, S. (1977). Social support and health. *Medical Care, 25*(Suppl.), 47–58.

Kazdin, C. (1988, June 28). Is this any way to grow old? *The New York Times,* A25.

Kaye, L. W. (1997). Informal caregiving by older men. In J. I. Kosberg & L. W. Kaye (Eds.), *Elderly Men* (pp. 231–249). New York: Springer Publishing.

Kosberg, J. I., & Kaye, L. W. (Eds.). (1997). *Elderly men: Special problems and professional challenges.* New York: Springer Publishing.

Kovar, M. G. (1980). Morbidity and health care utilization. In D. G. Haynes & M. Feinleib (Eds.), *Second conference on the epidemiology of aging.* Bethesda, MD: National Institutes of Health.

Kramer, A. M., Shaughnessy, P. W., & Pettigrew, M. L. (1985). Cost-effectiveness implications based on a comparison of nursing home and home health care mix. *Health Services Research, 20,* 387–406.

Krause, N. (1990). Perceived health problems, formal/informal support, and life satisfaction among older adults. *Journal of Gerontology, 45,* S193–205.

Krauss, N., Machlin, S., & Kass, B. (1999). *Use of health care services, 1996.* Rockville, MD: Agency for Health Care Policy and Research. MEPS Research Findings No.7. AHCPR Monograph, Pub. No. 99-0018.

Krout, J. A., Moen, P., Oggins, J., Holmes, H., & Bowen, N. (2000). Reasons for relocation to a continuing care retirement community. Retrieved September 8, 2002, from http://www.pathwayslifequalty.org/ wp00_04.html

Kutner, B., Franshel, D., Togo, A., & Langner, T. (1956). *Five hundred over sixty.* New York: Russel Sage Foundation.

Lachman, M. E., & James, J. (Eds.). (1997). *Multiple paths of midlife development.* Chicago: University of Chicago Press.

Lane, L. F. (1986). Paying for long-term care. *Retirement Planning, 12,* 8–10.

Lang, F. R., & Heckhausen, J. (2001) Perceived control over development and subjective well-being: Differential benefits across adulthood. *Journal of Personality and Social Psychology, 81,* 509–523.

Larson, R. (1978). Thirty years of research on the subjective well-being of older Americans. *Journal of Gerontology, 33,* 119–125.

Lawton, M. P. (1972). The dimensions of morale. In D. P. Kent, R. Kastenbaum, & S. Sherwood (Eds.), *Research Planning and Action for the Elderly.* New York: Behavioral Publications.

Lawton, M. P. (1975). The Philadelphia geriatric center morale scale: A revision. *Journal of Gerontology, 30,* 85–89.

Leibson, C. L., Garrard, J., Nitz, N., Waller, L., Indritz, M., Jackson, J., Rolnick, S. J., & Luepke, L. (1999). The role of depression in the association between self-rated physical health and clinically defined illness. *The Gerontologist, 39,* 291–298.

Lemon, B. W., Bengston, V. L., & Peterson, J. A. (1972). An exploration of the activity of theory of aging: Activity types and life satisfaction among in-movers to a retirement community. *Journal of Gerontology, 27,* 511–523.

Liang, J. (1984). Dimensions of the life satisfaction index A: A structural formulation. *Journal of Gerontology, 39,* 613–622.

Liang, J., & Bollen, K. A. (1983). The structure of the Philadelphia geriatric center morale scale: A reinterpretation. *Journal of Gerontology, 34,* 746–759.

Linn, B. S., & Linn, M. W. (1980). Objective and self-assessed health in the old and very old. *Social Science and Medicine, 14A,* 311–314.

Lohmann, N. (1977). Correlates of life satisfaction, morale and adjustment measures. *Journal of Gerontology, 43,* 54–60.

Lohr, M. J., Essex, M. J., & Klein, M. H. (1988). The relationships of coping responses to physical health status and life satisfaction among older women. *Journal of Gerontology, 43,* 54–60.

Lubitz, J. D. (1995). Longevity and Medicare expenditures. *New England Journal of Medicine, 332,* 999–1012.

Lysack, C. L., Neufeld, S. W., MacNeil, S. E., & Lichtenberg, P. A. (2001). At risk in old age: Elderly men who live alone. *Clinical Gerontologist, 24,* 77–96.

Maddox, G., & Eisdorfer, C. (1962). Some correlates of activity among the elderly. *Social Forces, 41,* 254–260.

Manton, K. G., & Gu, X. (2001). Changes in the prevalence of chronic disability in the United States black and non-black population above age 65 from 1982 to 1999. *Proceedings of the National Academy of Sciences, USA, 98,* 6354–6359.

Markides, K. S., & Martin, H. W. (1979). A causal model of life satisfaction among the elderly. *Journal of Gerontology, 34,* 86–93.

Matthias, R. E., Lubben, J. E., Atchison, K. A., & Schweitzer, S. O. (1997). Sexual activity and satisfaction among very old adults: Results from a community-dwelling Medicare population survey. *The Gerontologist, 37,* 6–14.

May, C. D. (1988, December 11). U.S. survey faults standards in nursing homes. *The New York Times,* B3.

McConnel, C. E. (1984). A note on the lifetime risk of nursing home residency. *The Gerontologist, 24,* 196–197.

McDowell, I., & Newell, C. (1996) *Measuring health* (2nd ed.). New York: Oxford University Press.

Mitchell, J. M., & Kemp, B. J. (2000). Quality of life in assisted living homes: A multidimensional analysis. *Journal of Gerontology, 55,* 117–127.

Monk, A. (1997). The transition to retirement. In J. I. Kosberg & L. W. Kaye (Eds.), *Elderly men* (pp. 144–158). New York: Springer Publishing.

Montauk, S. L. (1998). Home health care. *American Family Physician.* Retrieved September 8, 2002, from http://www.aafp.org/afp/981101ap/Montauk.html

Montgomery, R. (1982). A note on the lifetime risk of nursing home residency. *The Gerontologist 22,* 54–58.

Morris, J. N., & Sherwood, S. (1975). A retesting and modification of the Philadelphia geriatric center morale scale. *Journal of Gerontology, 30,* 77–84.

Morris, J. N., Wolf, R. S., & Klerman, L. V. (1975). Common themes among morale and depression scales. *Journal of Gerontology, 30,* 209–215.

Morrow-Howell, N., Proctor, E., Dore, R., & Kaplan, S. (1998). Post-acute services to older patients with heart disease. *Journal of Applied Gerontology, 17,* 150–171.

Mosher-Ashley, P. M., & Barrett, P. W. (1997). *A life worth living: Practical strategies for reducing depression in older adults.* Baltimore, MD: Health Professions Press.

Myers, D. G. (2000). The funds, friends, and faith of happy people. *American Psychologist, 55,* 56–67.

Myers, D. G., & Diener, E. (1995). Who is happy? *Psychological Science, 6,* 10–19.

Myles, J. F. (1970). Institutionalization and sick role identification among the elderly. *American Sociological Review, 431,* 508–520.

National Center for Health Statistics. (1978). Ambulatory Care Statistics Branch. Unpublished. Hyattsville, MD.

National Center for Health Statistics, Division of Health Care Statistics (1982a). *Health, United States, 1982.* Washington, DC: National Center for Health Statistics.

National Center for Health Statistics. (1999). *Health, United States, 1999, with Health and Aging Chartbook.* Hyattsville, MD: U.S. Department of Health and Human Services, (PHS) 99-1232.

Neugarten, B. L., Havighurst, R. J., & Tobin, S. S. (1961). The measurement of life satisfaction. *Journal of Gerontology, 16,* 134–143.

O'Connor, B. P. (1995). Family and friend relationships among older and younger adults: Interaction, motivation, mood, and quality. *International Journal of Aging and Human Development, 40,* 9–29.

O'Connor, B. P., & Vallerand, R. J. (1998) Psychological adjustment variables as predictors of mortality among nursing home residents. *Psychology and Aging, 13,* 368–374.

Okun, M. A. (1987). Life satisfaction. Maddox, G. L., Atchley, R. C., Poon, C. W., Roth, G. S., Siegler, I. C., & Steinberg, R. M. (Eds.), *The Encyclopedia of Aging.* New York: Springer Publishing.

Okun, M. A., & Stock, W. A. (1987). The construct validity of subjective well-being measures: An assessment via quantitive research syntheses. *Journal of Community Psychology, 15,* 487–492.

Pagel, M. D., Becker, J., & Coppel, D. B. (1985). Loss of control, self-blame, and depression: An investigation of spouse caregivers of

Alzheimer's disease patients. *Journal of Abnormal Psychology, 94,* 169–182.

Palmore, E. B. (1977). Facts on aging: A short quiz. *The Gerontologist, 17,* 315–320.

Palmore, E. B. (1980). The facts on aging quiz: A review of findings. *The Gerontologist 20,* 669–672.

Palmore, E. B. (1981). The facts on aging quiz: Part two. *The Gerontologist, 21,* 431–437.

Palmore, E. B. (1982). I. N. Osgood (Ed.), *Life after work.* New York: Praeger.

Palmore, E. B. (1984). The retired. In E. Palmore (Ed.), *Handbook on the aged in the United States.* Westport, CT: Greenwood Press.

Palmore, E. B., Cleveland, W. P., Nowlin, J. B., Ramm, D., & Steigler, I. C. (1979). Stress and adaptation in later life. *Journal of Gerontology, 34,* 841–851.

Palmore, E. B., & Kivett, V. (1977). Change in life satisfaction: A longitudinal study of persons aged 46–70. *Journal of Gerontology, 32,* 311–316.

Palmore, E. B., & Luikart, C. (1972). Health and social factors related to life satisfaction. *Journal of Health and Social Behavior, 13,* 68–80.

Penrod, J. D., Kane, R. L., Finch, M. D., & Kane, R. A. (1998). Effects of post-hospital Medicare home health and informal care on patient functional status. *Health Services Research, 33,* 513–529.

Pinquart, M., & Sorensen, S. (2000). Influences of socioeconomic status, social network, and competence on subjective well-being in later life: A meta-analysis. *Psychology and Aging, 15,* 187–224.

Pratt, C., Schmall, V., & Wright, S. (1987). Ethical concerns of family caregivers to dementia patients. *The Gerontologist, 27,* 632–638.

Pruchno, R. A., Peters, N. D., & Burant, C. J. (1995). Mental health of coresident family caregivers: Examination of a two-factor model. *Journal of Gerontology: Psychological Sciences, 50,* P247–P256.

Pruchno, R. A., & Rose, M. S. (2000). The effects of long-term care environments on health outcomes. *The Gerontologist, 40,* 422–428.

Pushkar, G. D., Feldman, R. M., Markiewicz, D., & Andres, D. (1995). When home caregiving ends: A longitudinal study of outcomes for caregivers of relatives with dementia. *Journal of the American Geriatrics Society, 43,* 10–16.

Quinn, J. F., & Berkhauser, R. V. (1994). Retirement and labor force participation of the elderly. In L. G. Martin & H. P. Samuel, (Eds.), *Demography of aging* (pp. 50–101). Washington, DC: National Academy Press.

Rapkin, B. D., & Fischer, K. (1992a). Personal goals of older adults: Issues in assessment and prediction. *Psychology and Aging, 7,* 127–137.

Rapkin, B. D., & Fischer, K. (1992b). Framing the construct of life satisfaction in terms of older adults' personal growth. *Psychology and Aging, 7,* 138–149.

Rife, J. C. (2001). Mental health benefits of part-time employment. *Clinical Gerontologist, 24,* 186–188.

Rimer, S. (1998, June 8). Families bear a bigger share of long-term care for the frail elderly. *New York Times,* p. A18.

Robinson, B. C. (1983). Characteristics of housebound elderly. Paper presented at the 36th Annual Meeting of Gerontological Society of America. San Francisco, CA.

Rosow, I. (1967). *Social integration of the aged.* New York: The Free Press.

Rowe, J. W., & Kahn, R. L. (1998). *Successful aging: The MacArthur Foundation study.* New York: Pantheon Books.

Salamon, M. J. (1985a). Sociocultural role theories in the elderly: A replication and extension. *Activities, Aging, and Development, 7,* 111–122.

Salamon, M. J. (1985b). Medication use and illness: The relationship between self and provider report. *Clinical Gerontologist, 3,* 17–22.

Salamon, M. J. (1987). Health care environment and life satisfaction in the elderly. *Journal of Aging Studies, 1,* 287–297.

Salamon, M. J. (1988). Measuring quality of life. *Clinical Gerontologist, 8,* 43–52.

Salamon, M. J. (1998). *Manual for the Life Satisfaction Scale (LSS); formerly LSES.* Hewlett, NY: Adult Developmental Center, Inc.

Salamon, M. J., & Conte, V. A. (1984). *The life satisfaction in the elderly scale.* Odessa, FL: Psychological Assessment Resources.

Salamon, M. J., & Conte, V. A. (1998). *Manual for the Life Satisfaction Scale (LSS).* Hewlett, NY: Adult Developmental Center, Inc.

Salamon, M. J., & Nichol, A. (1982). Rx for recreation: Part of the doctor's role. *Aging, 333–334,* 18–22.

Santor, D., Bagby, R. M., & Joffe, R. T. (1997). Evaluating stability and change in personality and depression. *Journal of Personality and Social Psychology, 73,* 1354–1360.

Sauer, W. J., & Warland, R. (1982). Morale and life satisfaction. In D. J. Mangen & W. A. Petersen (Eds.), *Research instruments in social gerontology: Clinical and social psychology* (Vol. 1). Minneapolis: University of Minnesota Press.

Savage, R. D. (1975). Psychometric techniques. In J. B. Howells (Ed.), *Modern perspectives in the psychiatry of old age.* New York: Brunner-Mazel.

Schaie, K. W., & Geiwitz, J. (1982). *Adult development and aging.* Boston, MA: Little Brown.

Schneider, E. L., & Brody, J. A. (1983). Aging, natural death and the compression of morbidity: Another view. *New England Journal of Medicine, 309,* 1016–1021.

Schwirian, P. M. (1982). Life satisfaction among nursing home residents. *Geriatric Nursing, 3,* 111–114.

Sheehy, G. (1986). *Passages.* New York: E. P. Dutton.

Shifren, K. (2001). Early caregiving and adult depression: Good news for young caregivers. *The Gerontologist, 41,* 188–190.

Silverman, A. G., Brahce, C. I., & Zielinski, C. (1981). *As parents grow older: A manual for program replication.* Ann Arbor: University of Michigan, Institute of Gerontology.

Sirocco, A. (1985). An overview of the 1982 national master facility inventory survey of nursing and related care homes. Advanced data from *Vital and Health Statistics, 11,* DMMS, (PMS) 85–1250.

Smith, K., & Bengston, V. L. (1979). Positive consequences of institutionalization: Solidarity between elderly parents and their middle-aged children. *The Gerontologist, 19,* 438–447.

Smith, P. C. (1988, April 3). Rising need for post-hospital care. *New York Times,* A1, 12.

Special Committee on Aging, United States Senate. (1986). *Nursing home care: The unfinished agenda.* Washington, DC: U.S. Government Printing Office.

Special Committee on Aging, United States Senate. (1977). *Medicine and aging: An assessment of opportunities and neglect.* Washington, DC: U.S. Government Printing Office.

Steinmetz, S. K. (1988). *Duty bound: Elder abuse and family care.* Newbury Park, CA: Sage.

Stevens, E. S. (1992). Reciprocity in social support: An advantage for the aging family. *Families in Society, 73,* 533–541.

Stone, R., Cafferata, G. L., & Sangl, J. (1987). Caregivers of the frail elderly: A national profile. *The Gerontologist, 27,* 616–626.

Strange, G. R., Chen, E. H., & Sanders, A. B. (1992). Use of emergency departments by elderly patients: Projections from a multicenter database. *Annals of Emergency Medicine, 21,* 819–824.

Strawbridge, W., & Wallhagen, M. (1992). Is all in the family always best? *Journal of Aging Studies, 6,* 81–92.

Stroebe, M. S., Hansson, R. O., Stroebe, W., & Schut, H. (Eds.). (2001). *Handbook of bereavement research: Consequences, coping, and care.* Washington, DC: American Psychological Association.

Tornatore, J. B., & Grant, L. A. (2002). Burden among family caregivers of persons with Alzheimer's disease in nursing homes. *The Gerontologist, 42,* 497–506.

U.S. Census Bureau (1982, October). Decennial censuses of population, 1900–1980 and projections of the population of the United States, 1982–2050. Series p-25, No. 922.

U.S. Department of Commerce, National Technical Information Service. (1999, February). NTIS. *Gerontology Assessment Resource Guide,* Milwaukee, WI: National Center for Cost Containment.

U.S. Department of Health, Education & Welfare. (1979). *National Nursing Home Survey.* Washington, DC: Office of Health Research Statistics and technology of the National Center of Health Statistics.

U.S. Health Care Financing Administration, Division of Medicaid Statistics. (1999). MSIS statistical report for federal fiscal year 1999. HCFA. Retrieved October 13, 2002 from http://www.hcfa.gov/Medicaid/ miss/mstats.htm

Utz, R. L., Carr, D., Neese, R., & Wortman, C. B. (2002). The effect of widowhood on older adults' social participation: An evaluation of activity, disengagement, and continuity theories. *The Gerontologist, 42*(4), 522–533.

Walshe, K., & Harrington, C. (2002). Regulation of nursing facilities in the United States: An analysis of resources and performance of state survey agencies. *The Gerontologist, 42,* 475–486.

Ward, R. A. (1979a). The meaning of voluntary association participation to older people. *Journal of Gerontology, 34,* 438–445.

Ward, R. A. (1979b). The never-married in later life. *Journal of Gerontology, 34,* 861–869.

Ware, J. E., Johnson, S. A., Davies-Avery, A., & Brook, R. H. (1979). *Conceptualization and measurement of health status for adults in the health insurance study* (Vol. III). Santa Monica, CA: Rand Corporation.

Welch, H. G., Wennberg, D. E., & Welch, W. P. (1996). The use of Medicare home health care services. *New England Journal of Medicine, 335,* 324–329.

What's New. (1984). *Geriatrics, 38,* 10–26.

What's New (1988). *Geriatrics, 43,* 16.

Willis, S. L., & Reid, J. D. (Eds.). (1999). *Life in the middle: Psychological and social development in the third quarter of life.* San Diego, CA: Academic Press.

Willits, F. K., & Crider, D. M. (1988). Health rating and life satisfaction in the later middle years. *Journal of Gerontology: Social Sciences, 43,* S172–S176.

Winokur, B., Black, D. W., & Nasrallah, A. (1988). Depressions secondary to other psychiatric disorders and medical illness. *American Journal of Psychiatry, 145,* 233–237.

Wunderlich, G. S., & Kohler, P. (Eds.). (2001). *Improving the quality of long-term care.* Washington, DC: National Academy of Sciences, Institute of Medicine.

York, J. (1984). Realistic expectations. Unpublished manuscript. Institute of Gerontology, University of Michigan.

Young, H. M. (1998). Moving to congregate housing: The last chosen home. *Journal of Aging Studies, 12,* 149–165.

Zarit, S. H. (1996). Interventions with family caregivers. In S. H. Zarit & B. G. Knight (Eds.), *A guide to psychotherapy and aging.* Washington, DC: American Psychological Association.

Zarit, S. H., Reever, K. E., & Bach-Peterson, J. (1980). Relatives of the impaired elderly: Correlates of feelings of burden. *The Gerontologist, 20,* 649–655.

Zarit, S. H., & Whitlach, C. J. (1992). Institutional placement: Phases of the transition. *The Gerontologist, 32,* 665–672.

Zika, S., & Chamberlain, K. (1992). On the relation between meaning in life and psychological well-being. *British Journal of Psychology, 83,* 133–145.

Index

Abnormal changes, 7–8
ACHCA, 79
Activities of daily living (ADL), 7, 43
Adjustment disorders, 36
ADL, 7, 43
Administration on Aging, 82
Administrator
    license, 69
    Aging. *See also* Elderly
    fear, 59–60
    life satisfaction, 11–12
    state offices, 82–90
    well-being, 11
Aging population
    demographics, 2–4
AHCA, 80
Alternate level of care, 21–22
Alzheimer's Disease and Related Disorders, 80
American Association of Homes for the Aging, 69, 79
American Association of Retired Persons, 80–81
American College of Health Care Administrators (ACHCA), 79
American Foundation for the Blind, 81
American Health Care Association (AHCA), 80

American Nursing Home Association, 69
Assisted living, 23–25
Attitude
    hospitals, 21
    patients
        toward nursing home, 47–50
Audiology, *xii*

Bathroom
    access to, 58
Beds
    hospital, 58
Beliefs, *xi*
Belongings. *See* Possessions
Biological changes
    normal, 4–5
Board of Nursing Home Administrators, 80
Bone
    strength loss, 4–5

Cardiovascular system
    slowing down, 4–5
Caregiver
    denies own needs, 35
    emotional stability, 59
Caregivers
    relief for, 59
Cavan Attitude Inventory, 37, 38
Cavan Scale, 38

Springer Publishing Company

Innovative Interventions to Reduce Dementia Caregiver Distress
A Clinical Guide

David W. Coon, PhD,
Dolores Gallagher-Thompson, PhD, ABPP,
and **Larry W. Thompson,** PhD, Editors

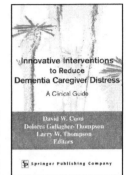

This volume provides an overview of emerging themes in dementia caregiving research and presents a broad array of practical strategies for reducing caregiver distress, including interventions for specific populations such as ethnic minority caregivers, male caregivers, and caregivers with diverse sexual orientations. Innovative approaches include partnering with primary care physicians to improve quality of life for both patient and caregiver, and the use of technological advances to help distressed caregivers.

Partial Contents:

Part I: Background Issues
- Family Caregivers: Enduring and Emergent Themes, *D.W. Coon, M.G. Ory, and R. Schulz*
- Monitoring and Evaluating Interventions, *B.H. Gottlieb, L.W. Thompson, D. Gallagher-Thompson, and M. Bourgeois*

Part II: Practical Interventions for the Reduction of Caregiver Distress: Experience from the Field
- Specific Stressors of Spousal Caregivers: Difficult Behaviors, Loss of Sexual Intimacy, and Incontinence, *M. Mittelman, A. Zeiss, H. Davies, et al.*
- Family Interventions to Address the Needs of the Caregiving System, *S. Arguelles, E. Klausner, T. Arguelles, et al.*

Part III: Case Examples of Interventions Tailored to Specific Caregiving Groups
- Ethnic Minority Caregivers, *E. Edgerly, L. Montes, E. Yau, et al.*
- Male Caregivers: Challenges and Opportunities, *S.A. Lauderdale, J.A. D'Andrea, and D.W. Coon*

Part IV: Recommendations for the Future
- Future Directions in Dementia Caregiving Intervention Research and Practice, *L.W. Thompson, D. Gallagher-Thompson, et al.*

2003   328pp   0-8261-4801-8   hard

---

536 Broadway, New York, NY 10012 • (212) 431-4370 • Fax (212) 941-7842
Order Toll-Free: 877-687-7476 • Order on-line: www.springerpub.com

Springer Publishing Company

Aging Independently
Living Arrangements and Mobility

K. Warner Schaie, PhD, Hans-Werner Wahl, Dr phil,
Heidrun Mollenkopf, Dr phil, and Frank Oswald, Dr phil, Editors

"This outstanding volume has something to offer geriatric and gerontological practitioners of every type and stripe— researchers, program planners and administrators, policy makers, environmental engineers, caregivers, community housing specialists, and health service professionals."
—**Rick H. Scheidt**, PhD
School of Family Studies and Human Services
Kansas State University

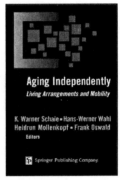

Based on the conference *"Aging in the Community: Living Arrangements and Mobility,"* this volume compares living arrangements and outdoor mobility within German and American cultures and explores the impact on older persons' critical roles in community life and sustainable community development. The book leads us to a new understanding of distance and nearness even in the presence of severe chronic illness.

Partial Contents:
Section I: Setting the Field • Research on Living Arrangements in Old Age for What? *H.W. Wahl* • Mobility for What? *K.W. Schaie*

Section II: The Aging Individual and the Environment - Basic Considerations • Enabling Environments for Physical Aging: A Balance of Preventive and Compensatory Interventions, *J.D. Fozard* • Psychological Issues of Aging in the Community, *A. Kruse*

Section III: Aging in the Community "Indoor": Living Arrangements • Purpose-Built Housing and Home Adaptations for Older Adults: The American Perspective, *V. Regnier* • Creating Places for People With Dementia: An Action Research Perspective, *G.D. Weisman*

Section IV: Aging in the Community "Outdoor": Mobility • Impact of Transportation Systems on Mobility of Elderly Persons in Germany, *H. Mollenkopf* • Macro-Interventions: Roads, Transportation Systems, Traffic Calming, and Vehicle Design, *P.P. Jovanis*

Section V: Future Perspectives of Aging in the Community Combining Perspectives of Aging Inside and Outside the Home • Future Developments in Living Environments for Older People in the U.S. and Germany, *H.W. Wahl and L.N. Gitlin*

2003   376pp   0-8261-1854-2   hard

536 Broadway, New York, NY 10012 • **(212) 431-4370** • **Fax (212) 941-7842**
Order Toll-Free: 877-687-7476 • **Order on-line: www.springerpub.com**

Springer Publishing Company

Home Care Advances

Essential Research and Policy Issues

Robert H. Binstock, PhD, and **Leighton E. Cluff,** MD, Editors

"An important and illuminating book . . . Experts address the important issues . . . complex relations between families and paid caregivers . . . aspects of the home care business . . . the role of hospice care."
— **Robert N. Butler,** MD
President, International Longevity Center
Geriatrics Professor, Mount Sinai Medical Center

This volume, edited by the most prominent gerontologists in the field, contains the latest research and policy advances on the efficacy of the fastest growing segment within the health delivery system today—home care. The opening section of this book provides an introductory landscape of home care in the US and how it has evolved to the present day. The next section sets forth a series of perspectives on the provision of home care technology, computers, and other communication technologies. Section three deals with aspects of financing, auspices, and quality of care. The volume concludes by assessing the future of home care from a public policy perspective.

Contents:
• Issues and Challenges in Home Care
• The Changing Health and Social Environments of Home Care
• The Use of Technology in Home Care
• Families and Paid Workers: The Complexities of Home Care Roles
• Hospice: End-of-Life Care at Home
• Home Care as a Business
• Issues in Understanding Resource Consumption in Publicly Funded Home Care
• Shaping Home Care by Measuring Outcomes
• Testing Home Care as a Managed Care Intervention Weaver
• Assuring Quality in Care at Home
• The Uncertain Future of Home Care

2000   280pp   0-8261-1304-4   hard

536 Broadway, New York, NY 10012 • (212) 431-4370 • Fax (212) 941-7842
Order Toll-Free: 877-687-7476 • Order on-line: www.springerpub.com